The Eden Conspiracy

Ancient memories of ET contact

and the Bible before God

What people are saying about Paul's Books

Paul Anthony Wallis is one of my best colleagues...a very intelligent and clever personality and a brilliant author of books. I just came to his books later! Paul's way of seeing things, his arguments and his proofs are enlightening. It will be the new understanding of our world and our religion. Paul has a way of speaking that everyone can understand. His documentaries and philosophies are watched by millions worldwide. I have full respect for him. **Erich von Daniken – Chariots *of the* Gods *(on the Chariots of the Gods Podcast)***

Paul Wallis takes us on a journey that we will never forget. This generation's "Chariots of the Gods!" **George Noory – Coast *to* Coast, Beyond Belief**

It is a great pleasure to collaborate with Paul. Paul's contribution is excellent and for me it is important to compare my studies with Paul's! Though far apart geographically we are spiritually close! We are a good team. **Mauro Biglino**

A remarkable orator. I appreciate it that Paul has the courage to speak publicly and make himself vulnerable to criticism. He is a courageous soul for having done that and we all get to benefit from it. For anyone interested in the cross-over of religion and ET's, Paul's work is a must-read. **Regina Meredith, *Open Minds* GAIA TV**

Paul is doing a courageous service [giving] us a new perspective on the creation and engineering of man. **Sean Stone – Actor, Media Host**

Paul is an extraordinary researcher who radiates tranquillity, scholarship and courage. He has walked the talk and visited [so many] great places and been in contact with some great researchers. Paul Wallis does the footwork, and it really shows in his scholarship. **Revd Dr Sean O'Laoire PhD**

Paul's wit and humility are second only to his deep knowledge regarding the esoteric nature of human history and mankind's origins. I strongly recommend reading his books to gain a holistic perspective which elegantly bridges spirituality and religion via the connection of higher consciousness.
Jay Campbell – Researcher, Bestselling Author.

There's a ton of stuff in here. I have to recommend it.
Benjamin Grundy – Mysterious Universe

Paul Wallis expresses the awareness of many cultures in such a personable way. Really fascinating. I have learned so much.
Barbara Lamb – Licensed Psychotherapist

Very few scholars embedded so deeply in the church have ever exhibited the courage to question their chosen path. We highly recommend Paul's extraordinary works of investigation to all those seeking a more enlightened path of living.
Jaimie and Aspasia Leonarder – The Movie Show SBS, VP & Secretary of U.F.O. Research New South Wales

"I have read many books on contact. Paul's books are of a completely different ilk. They come with so much credibility, so much research, and so much to back them up. To anyone wanting to know about ET's and asking, 'What's the truth?' I would say, 'Read Paul's books!'" **Sandra Sedgbeer (OM Times)**

Also by this Author

Escaping from Eden

ISBN: 978 1 78904 387 7

The Scars of Eden

ISBN: 978 1 78904 852 0

Echoes of Eden

ISBN: 978 0 6454183 0 9

Paul Wallis Books

First published by Paul Wallis Books, 2023

www.paulanthonywallis.com

Text copyright: Paul Wallis 2023

ISBN: 978 0 6454183 2 3

ISBN: 978 0 6454183 3 0 (e-book)

Design: tempting_dezine

The Eden Conspiracy

Ancient memories of ET contact and the Bible
before God

Paul Wallis

Paul Wallis Books

Acknowledgments

This book owes its existence to the generous encouragement of my beautiful family, Ruth, Evie, Ben, Caleb, Hugo, and Skye, and of my *5th Kind TV* collaborator Anthony Barrett. I am also deeply indebted to fellow explorers Erich Von Daniken, Ramon Zurcher, George Noory, Joan Miller, Omar Faizi of Watchers Talk, Neil Gaur of Portal to Ascension, Steven and Evan Strong of *Our Alien Ancestry*, Sandra Sedgbeer of *OM Times*, Professor Brigadier General Haim Eshed, David Lovegrove, and Raanen Shaked and Gabriel Beharlia of the newspaper *Yediot Aharanot*, my guide Massillon, and to my friend Philip Atkinson for sharing his story with me. As always, personal stories and exchanges are variously conflated and relocated with names altered to protect the anonymity of those who have entrusted me with their stories.

We are indebted to archaeologists like Roland de Vaux, Edwin Shook, William Coe, George Guillemin, and William Dever, and Assyriologists like George Smith, Nathaniel Schmidt and the wonderful Irving Finkel, whose work offers us glimpses into the worlds of our ancestors, and to pioneers of Biblical analysis in the lane of Jean Astruc, Julius Wellhausen, Karl Heinrich Graf and Wilhelm Vatke, who were willing to blaze a trail where angels fear to tread. I would also like to express my personal thanks to my dear friends Mauro Biglino and Elisabetta Soro without whose encouragement and serial collaboration on *The 5th Kind*, this book would not be in your hands right now. As Mauro says, *"We are geographically far apart, but spiritually close!"*

I am enormously grateful to the many who have read, liked and shared my content in book and electronic form, and who have helped to propel www.paulanthonywallis.com the *Paul Wallis Channel* and *5thKind.TV* to even wider audiences.

When I was eleven, my mother bought me a book, titled, *"An Atlas of World Mysteries."* It looked at mysteries which had already captured my youthful imagination, The Loch Ness Monster, the Bermuda Triangle, Stonehenge. It contained other mysteries about which I had never even heard, cryptids, the pyramids of the world, and the theories of Velikovsky. The author, Francis Hitching, didn't seek to settle every controversy or explain every anomaly away. He simply pointed me to clues that not everything in our past has yet been understood or explained. By giving me that book my mother had found a wonderful way to encourage my youthful curiosity and keep me from ever settling for non-explanations of the mysteries of life. Without that book, and my mum and dad's copy of Erich von Daniken's iconic oeuvre *Chariots of the Gods*, my curiosity may not have led me into thirty-three years of work as a church doctor and on into the territory of paleocontact, indigenous narratives and human potential.

So I acknowledge with thanks my parents, Rodney and Brenda, and my brother Mark whose curiosity finds fascination in all the same areas I do. Another member of my family who deserves special mention is my daughter, Evie. Often while driving, I suddenly work out how to express a thought in coherent English. In those moments it has been Evie, patiently taking dictation on old receipts and shopping lists, who has committed my words to paper. Thank you Evie! Thanks are also due to my parents-in-law Kofi and Patience, whose education in Ghanaian history and culture has been invaluable. I dedicate *The Eden Conspiracy* to every one of my coaching clients, pastors, politicians, students, doctors, tradies – beautiful people of every background. And to all who, privately or publicly, wrestle with the implications of paleocontact, I salute you.

Introduction and Chapter One

Meet Me in Brazil

Nobody likes to be vomited on. It's the heat of it I feel first, then everything else - which I will leave to your imagination. The vomit isn't mine. It belongs to an innocent-looking blonde-haired girl, standing next to me in the hot and crowded bus to Pesqueira. We are only fifteen minutes into a three-hour drive into the interior, on what is, even at this early hour, a steaming, hot day in Pernambuco, Brazil. It's going to be a long journey.

Then something wonderful happens. A small group of older women around me springs into action. The girl's mother begins nursing her needs next to me, while another woman establishes that my limited grasp of Brasileiro requires that sign language will be the best approach to guide me through the next necessary steps. Through a sequence of hand gestures, this second lady indicates that my injured pants and boots have to come off. These are then carefully passed to a woman seated next to the open window, where they intercept with a large bottle of water. This last member of our *ad hoc* team now works out a way to rinse all the visible offence from my items without spraying anyone else – quite a feat in itself – at which point a plastic carrier bag joins the fray, a gift from another contributor, allowing us to seal off the offending items to store them for future use.

What began as a horribly embarrassing moment has been transformed by the dense crowd of women occupying my part of the bus into a moment of caring, intelligent community, and I feel uplifted by their kindness and rather less self-conscious than I might have expected, surrounded by all this positive female energy.

Being barefoot, less dressed, and not as fresh smelling as I would have preferred, I can't help feeling that I am cutting an unimpressive figure as I finally disembark the bus to meet my Brazilian hosts at Pesqueira, somehow still hoping to make a positive first impression. Secretly, inside, I am doing my best to ignore that I am feeling a long way from home. However, by the time I have reunited with my luggage, found some clean clothes and footwear, and freshened myself up, the genuine warmth of my hosts and the pleasant atmosphere of the town have more than restored my spirits.

Augusto is my guide, and he enthusiastically ferries me to the first event of the festival, eager to introduce me to the culture of his hometown. The whole town is a party tonight. I have never experienced anything like it. Food stalls line the streets. Everywhere there is music. In every square there is dancing, and the atmosphere of joy and celebration is absolutely infectious. Every person I encounter is so friendly and enthusiastic and, as the evening progresses, I feel like I have made a whole city's worth of new friends.

If you have read *Echoes of Eden*, you will have recognized Augusto, my young Brazilian guide, and you will know what is about to happen. You will already know that within a few hours tonight's festivities will lay something into my Christian worldview which, like a depth-charge, will blow apart many of my naïve faith-based assumptions about the world. But don't skip ahead, because in the next few pages, I will take us deeper into the twists and turns of my epiphany in the jungles, favelas, and cities of Amazonia. A few pages from now you will see why I have brought us back to Brazil where we last met. If, on the other hand, you have not yet visited this beautiful country with me, then the encounter that follows will probably have you as confused as I was at the time, as my neat and tidy Christian worldview began to spin around, crack open, and reveal glimpses of a whole other layer of human story.

"You have come to my town at the perfect time!" says Augusto. *"This is our corn festival!"* It clearly is. As I look around, corn is everywhere to be seen, transformed into all kinds of foods, savouries, desserts, drinks, and decorations. Every table I see seems to have corn cakes on it to mark the occasion. *"It is like a harvest festival where we celebrate the gift of corn."*

As the evening progresses the party transforms into a procession, in which corn figurines, both hand-held and woven into headwear, are slowly being carried towards and into the cathedral, with candles held high and the fragrant aromas of incense filling the night air. Eager to practice my newly acquired Brasileiro, I ask my new friends what is going to happen next. *"Tonight, we are thanking the Queen of Heaven for the gift of corn. It is very important because without that gift none of us would be alive."*

Once in the church, proceedings take on a more familiar tone. I am partway through my training to become an Anglican priest. So, the Catholic liturgy of the mass which commences as the clock strikes midnight has a somewhat familiar shape and I think I have my head around what's going on. But I don't. Not by a long chalk.

The following morning, Augusto and I sit down with a cup of strong coffee, brewed by our host, Rita, on the gas stove in the rear courtyard of her historic home in the city's central district. Augusto is a twenty-something year-old trainee priest with the Anglican Church in Brazil. A friend of a friend selected him to assist me with my mission which, as part of my bachelor's degree, is to expose myself to the current evolution of organized Christianity in Brazil and return to the UK with a long theological treatise for my college tutors to critique.

"So, Paul," Augusto sits, cross-legged on the chair opposite mine, and I can see that he is already relishing his role as my tutor, *"How did you enjoy our festival last night?"*

"I thought it was wonderful. I have been to quite a few harvest festivals in England, and I can tell you they're not like that! Last night's event was so vibrant and joyful. It was fun. And people had gone to so much effort with the corn decorations, the foods, the costumes and everything. They obviously took it very seriously. Clearly, the corn harvest is an important event in the Catholic calendar here."

"Yes, Paul. But I need to correct you. That was not a Roman Catholic event."

My brow furrows and I peer at Augusto, thinking he has challenged me with a riddle of some kind. Augusto peers at me as if he expects me to reply with sudden understanding. However, the penny has not yet dropped. Augusto continues.

"Nothing that happened outside the Church before we went in for the mass has anything to do with Roman Catholic religion."

"What was it then?"

"We were thanking the Queen of Heaven for giving our ancestors the gift of corn."

My mental wheels are slowly turning.

"Thousands of years ago our ancestors learned to cultivate crops and were taught how to transform corn into food. Without the gift of agriculture, you can only live like a forager, in a very primitive way, just surviving. The gift of cultivation changes everything. All this happened when the Queen of Heaven came to Earth from the heavens and gave our ancestors this great gift."

Thousands of years ago? The Queen of Heaven? To my knowledge the Queen of Heaven was a title given by the Roman Catholic church to Mary, the mother of Jesus. According to the story I knew, Mary lived in Palestine in the first century of the common era and was certainly not in Brazil, least of all *"thousands of years ago,"* let alone delivering crash courses in agricultural science. So, whoever Augusto's prehistoric interloper was, it surely had to be someone else.

"The new Pope does not like our local ceremonies here. His men want to clean up our harvest festivals and make them more Catholic. Many of the other things you saw, the corn figurines, the songs, the dances, the cleaning of the steps at the entrance of the cathedral, His Holiness wants it all stopped. The whole story we are remembering concerning our ancestors, John Paul wants us to erase because it is not a Catholic story."

"But look around at my neighbours, Paul. My ancestors are from the interior, so they carry all the memory and rituals of our indigenous ancestors. Many of us have ancestors who came here from West Africa when people were kidnapped and brought here to slave in the sugar plantations. So, our people also carry memory and ritual from Africa. That's why in my family, and in many families in this region, we still remember this amazing moment from thousands of years ago. We celebrate because it reminds us of who we are, where we came from and how our ancestors became a civilization. Meanwhile, His Holiness wants us to throw away our indigenous Amazonian heritage and throw away our African heritage. He wants our children to know only the European Catholicism that came from Portugal, and to forget everything else. But many of the people here don't want to do that. Because it is our family heritage. It is about who we are."

This motif of the new Pope *"cleaning up"* Brazilian culture was a theme which I would hear repeating throughout my months of

17

travel and exploration through the towns and cities of 1980's Amazonia. In every place, I found grassroots initiatives being marginalized, excluded, and replaced with top-down, priest-centered hierarchy. The blossoming of peer-to-peer Christian communities among the poorest of Brazilians living in the interior was an inspiring phenomenon to me, and to many Christians around the world. But at ground level I could see this grassroots energy was being trammeled by the institution, stifled with regulation, and progressively shut down. It was through the young eyes of an English evangelical believer that I noticed these dynamics and sided with my friends who were champions of the grassroots.

But what I failed to perceive at the time were the cosmic implications of what Augusto had just told me. The information, carried so faithfully in the indigenous Amazonian and West African story was information about a profound moment in our development as a species recalled by cultures all around the world. It is a moment we call the Great Leap Forward. Cultivation of crops is the bedrock of civilization. It means surpluses. Surpluses mean that people can settle, build towns and cities, and move from a life of animal subsistence to the life of a specialized society. Such specialization is the prerequisite to all subsequent technological progress. Here, apparently, it was the Queen of Heaven who enabled the Great Leap Forward. Travelling further north into Guatemala I would hear of Hun Hunapu. If I travelled to ancient Greece, I would hear about Aphrodite. If I continued on to ancient Rome, I would be told the stories of Venus. From ancient Babylon I would hear the story of Oannes and the Apkallu. Ancient Sumerians would tell me the story of Shamhat. In Mali West Africa I would be taught about the Nommos, in Nigeria I would learn about the first female who brought farming to humanity. She was the creation of beings called Abassi and Atai. In Southern Africa, Zulu sisters and brothers would teach me

18

about the origins of humanity with the male Unkulunkulu, and the origins of agriculture with the female Mbab Mwane Waresa. In a later chapter a young man of the Yolngu people in Australia's Northern Territory will add an even more mysterious layer to the story. But the long and short of it is that all around the world, this Great Leap Forward is credited to predominantly female, non-human visitors.

Beyond identifying our helpers as advanced non-human beings, some of those cultures are quite specific about where these ancient tutors came from. The Efik and Zulu stories report that our ancient tutors came from the stars. Aboriginal Australian story and narratives of the Cherokee in North America specify the Pleiades. The Dogon people of Mali specify the Sirius star system. The Babylonians add the detail that our visitors' bases on planet Earth are hidden beneath the waters of our lakes and oceans. All these narratives are stories of our ancestors' first contact with visitors who, today, we would call *extra-terrestrials*. Our intersection with those visitors in the deep past is called *paleocontact*.

If I had no awareness of this body of cultural memory concerning the Great Leap Forward, I had even less awareness that this same memory echoes through the pages of the Bible itself. And not in some vague way. Just like these other cultures the Bible names the beings who sat with our ancestors and gave them the nurture and tuition which transformed them into farmers, city-builders, and civilization makers. It too speaks of the stellar origins of our ancient visitors and names their home constellations. Yet at this stage in my young career as a student of theology, none of this information had found its way into our curriculum at college. I literally had no idea.

Today my work lies in uncovering and exploring these ancient world narratives concerning ET contact in our ancestral past. It is work which has transformed my life from that of a mainstream senior churchman to a front man for controversy and close encounters, ancient and modern.

In the thirty-three years before becoming known as the author of *"This Generation's Chariots of the Gods"* (and I have George Noory of *Coast to Coast* to thank for that accolade) I enjoyed a long and interesting career as a church doctor, troubleshooting for communities of faith, culminating in my appointment as an Archdeacon for the Anglican Church in Australia. An archdeacon is one down from a bishop, there to facilitate transitions, oversight clergy and troubleshoot in communities of faith. My journey into this controversial territory was via another of my roles in church life. For fifteen years, as a theological educator, I trained pastors in the history of Christian thought and in hermeneutics – the principles of interpreting ancient texts – the Bible in particular. It was through applying those principles of interpretation to anomalies in the Bible's stories of origins that a hidden layer of the Bible's story began to open up to me.

My discovery has cost me a few friends, income, and employment opportunities. But I wouldn't trade for the world all that I have gained through my study of what for so long has been such a great taboo. Through my books *Escaping from Eden, The Scars of Eden* and *Echoes of Eden,* I share the incredible journey that took me from mainstream Christian orthodoxy to this controversial layer of story, almost excised from Christian memory. Almost, but not entirely. Because it's there in the early church fathers. And it's there in the Bible - the Hebrew story of Paleocontact.

For hundreds and thousands of years believers have turned to the Hebrew Scriptures for insights on God, the universe and everything. We take it for granted that the Bible is, from cover to cover, a book about God. People call it *"God's book."* However, my *Eden* series has persuaded many around the world, people of every cultural and spiritual background, that the Bible was originally about something else, and that its pages are, in reality, full of paleocontact. It is no exaggeration to say that this conclusion has changed my life.

In the pages that follow, I will take you on a journey to another time and another place. Together we will discover what the Bible was about before its narratives of paleocontact were translated out of plain sight. In its pre-edited form, what was it that the ancient Hebrew authors wanted us to know? What were the sights and sounds they wanted to share with us? And what exactly was the message of it all before it morphed into a call for meek and obedient monotheism?

As we tour the Levant, ancient Sumeria and Babylonia with forays into North America, Greece, Italy, Israel, Egypt, West Africa, Papua New Guinea, and my own backyard in Australia, we will discover how religious and civic authorities through the ages have distorted the transmission of the Bible in such a way as to conceal vital information concerning who we are as a species and how much we are capable of. Together we will lift the lid on secrets gifted to posterity by our Hebrew ancestors, whose intent was to equip future generations to shape a better human experience. These lost truths reveal that, as individuals and as societies, we have the capacity for so much more than the later, God-oriented translations have taught us to believe.

If this sounds far-fetched, I am going to keep our feet on the ground by continually touching base with the root meanings of a sequence of key words which punctuate the ancient texts of the Bible. These root meanings will be our stepping-stones. They are the juicy kernel of Hebrew words like *seba hassamayim, elyon, olam, kavod, ruach, el shaddai, Yahweh, Asherah* and *elohim*. The mistranslation of these vital words has distorted not only the religions of the Bible, but the psychology of every society whose cultures have been shaped by the thought and mores of Judaism and Christianity. In the chapter ashead you will see how the realm of root meanings opens up a whole world of lost memory. If you are willing to share the journey with me and boldly enter this strange new world, then together we will unearth powerful information about the origins of our species and our geopolitical environment. We will unlock information about our forgotten past and our potential today.

Augusto was right. This is not the Roman Catholic story. On the contrary, these are the ancestral narratives which the administration of Pope John Paul II was trying so hard to delete from the memories of the faithful in twentieth century Brazil. Incidentally, it is the same information glancingly referenced in U.S. Congressional hearings in 2022, arising from the Senate briefing of 2021, which have authenticated UFO contact phenomena in the present day. The public struggle in the U.S. among the powers of the Senate, Congress and the Pentagon concerning those hearings is just one manifestation of a conflict that is ages old. It is the struggle among those who govern us to shape and police what information is open to the public and what is not. Of course all governments want dominance over the public conversation. It's only natural. To use today's language, every power wishes to *"control the narrative."*

This is exactly what I witnessed first-hand, as a naïve, young traveler back in the day, as I pursued my theological research among the towns, villages, and favelas of Amazonia. There I was able to see, in the flesh, a process of suppression of old narratives for deletion and replacement with official narratives. In Amazonia I was able to observe in real time as a papal administration did its level best to dematerialize the corn figurines, the cultural songs, together with stories and rituals which carried the local culture's memories of paleocontact. What I had no idea of at the time was that this papal clean-up was only one moment in a brutal and long-lived process of thought-control, a process which has been continuous since before the Roman Catholic Church was even conceived of. In the chapters ahead, we will see that Pope John Paul's liturgical enforcers were not the first regime to try and delete a whole world of ancestral memory. Not by a long chalk. Not by thousands of years.

Chapter Two

Bread Cakes and Standing Stones

Tel Arad, the Negev Desert – 16 miles west of the Dead Sea

"The whole town is a party tonight. Food stalls line the streets and everywhere there is music. Every table has corn cakes on it to mark today's festival and the feeling of joy and celebration fills the city. It is the harvest festival. In the afternoon the whole crowd will form a procession, and we will carry our figurines to the temple, where the fragrant smell of incense already fills the air."

"Our clay figurines show a voluptuous woman with bouffant hair and bare breasts. She is the Queen of Heaven who visited our distant ancestors, and sat with our ancient elders, teaching them all the secrets of farming, the cultivation of crops, and the secrets of animal husbandry. She turned our ancestors from wandering nomads into settled farmers and patriarchs of cities. Without The Queen of Heaven, we would not be here. She is the mother of civilization. And today we are giving thanks."

But wait a minute! Does this sound like a repeat? You may be wondering if my editor has missed an accidental duplication here. But this is not Amazonia. In fact, we are nowhere even close to Brazil. Tel Arad is in the Levant, a town and district near Jerusalem. And the liturgical reformers who, before the festival did their best to seize the clay figurines and break off their heads, are not papal officers for John Paul II. They are the deputies of King Josiah and the High Priestly family in Jerusalem. Neither is this the 1980's. We are at some point in the C7thBCE. At this time and in this place, the name of the Queen of Heaven is not Mary. It is Asherah.

"Asherah has been part of our people's memory and ritual for as long as anyone in this corner of the Empire can remember. Every harvest festival we remember the moment when she first arrived and chose our people to lift us up and establish us as a civilization on Earth. To us, Asherah represents fertility and life. She is the Lion Lady, the Queen of Heaven."

"Throughout the land of Judea are many sacred sites, temples built to house our altars and standing stones. The purpose of standing stones is to mark the places of first contact. They commemorate where we were when we first met our helpers from the stars. For instance, when our ancestor Jacob encountered powerful beings descending to Earth from the stars and then returning to the stars by the means of the mysterious 'ladder,' he built an altar to mark the place and commemorate his encounter. He also built a temple for the altar and called it Bethel, which is short for the home or 'Place of the Powerful Ones.'"

"Here at Tel Arad, we erected three standing stones, including one for Yahweh and one for Asherah. We also have two altars, and like many other towns we have made ours a part of our local temple. It may not be as old as the Temple at Bethel, or as grand as the Temple of Solomon, or the Temple at Dan, with its five standing stones and two high places. Nevertheless, ours has everything the same, only smaller. We have a courtyard with an altar, a great room and a holy of holies, the inner sanctuary."

"We are very proud of our temple and our priestly family, but we can see where these royal and high priestly visits are leading. By the reckoning of the Jerusalem authorities, the powerful ones from the stars are no longer considered worthy of recollection. This year they are breaking the heads off our Asherah figures. Next year the King's soldiers and the Temple Guard will return to knock down our standing stones. Perhaps the year after they will be back again to break off the horns of our altars."

"For me it is a sad thing to think that the magnificent high places throughout the region are no longer viewed as sacred or acceptable by our leaders in Jerusalem. 'Idols,' they call them. And we all know that idolatry is a sin. The word from Jerusalem is that one God, one King, one Temple, and one High Priest are quite sufficient."

"Of course, the priestly families scattered across the region take a different view. Here at Tel Arad our priests whisper quietly that standing stones once knocked down can be put back up. Broken figurines can be replaced. I know that at Taanach to the north they have a beautiful mold for making reproductions of Asherah. So, we can certainly make more. At Tel El Farah, in Idalion, in the Transjordan, and as far away as Cyprus, where they call Asherah 'Hathor,' they have carvings of the mysterious doorways through which the Queen of Heaven arrived in the beginning. Will the King's soldiers and the Jerusalem Temple Guard pull every one of them down?"

"In every place where Jewish men sign their inscriptions as 'A Son of Anat and Servant of the Lion Lady,' will the Jerusalem Guard deface every inscription? Surely, they cannot destroy every single one. Do you think they can seize every shiny pendant of Asherah-Hathor, worn by our neighbours at Ugarit and Minet el Bedha? Do the authorities really think they can make us all forget? No. Surely not. We remember Asherah here. She showed us the secrets of life, taught us to become a civilization and rise as a nation. She is the great Mother of my people. We cannot forget her."

The answer to our narrator's question is *yes* and *no*. Yes, the Jerusalem Guard really will break the altars of the other Jewish temples, tear down their standing stones, confiscate and break off the heads of their clay figurines, in a desperate attempt to erase the memory of the Elat / The Lion Lady / Hathor / Anat / Astarte /

27

Asherah. But no, in the end they will not succeed. Ultimately, they will fail because the memory of Asherah in all her incarnations is simply too pervasive throughout Judea, as well as in countries beyond, such as Syria, Cyprus and Phoenicia.

II Kings 17:10 gives us a picture of just how widespread Asherah's influence was. Here the redactor offers us a perspective on Asherah from the other side of the coin. This is the vantage of the Yahwist Temple and Court in Jerusalem. It is why the narrator of II Kings 17 simultaneously describes and condemns the Jewish people's commemoration of Asherah and other powerful entities. Having served as a pastor for thirty-three years, I have preached many times through the Hebrew Canon. Yet somehow, I had always missed the elephant in this text. Like many preachers, my general approach through the years was to calculate the author's intent, and then convey a similar message to my audience. However, studying a text for a sermon and studying a text to unpack a full and accurate picture of the past are not always the same thing.

Today I am asking different questions. I will allow myself to separate the narrator's evaluation of the people's practices from his actual description of them. When I make this separation, a picture emerges revealing what Judaism actually looked like in the C8thBCE, and it has taken me completely by surprise.

"The Israelites...worshipped...other Powerful Ones."

This is shocking. Let that information sink in. What C8thBCE Judaism actually was and what the writer of II Kings thought it should be were two completely different things.

"The Israelites...worshipped...other Powerful Ones. [They] spoke disparagingly of their Powerful One Yahweh...They built high places (ie temples commemorating other Powerful Ones) in every

place they lived, from every watchtower to every fortified town. They set up standing stones and Asherahs on every high hill and under every green tree."

Suddenly, I can see clearly how deeply embedded the narrative of paleocontact really was in ancient Judaism. It was not marginal. The erection of Asherahs, standing stones, high places, and temples memorializing other powerful beings was mainstream Jewish practice. In fact, the prophet Jeremiah, writing in the C7th-6thBCE, lamented the fact that this was Jewish practice *"on every high hill, and under every green tree."* (Jeremiah 2:20, 3:6) Similarly, II Kings 17 tells us that this was Jewish practice *"in every place they lived."*

Put alongside each other, these phrases give a clear and unmistakable picture: *"From every watchtower to every fortified town…"* and *"on every high hill and under every green tree"* and *"in every place they lived."* This is how normal the commemoration of Asherah and other advanced beings really was to mainstream Judaism at that time. This was nothing like how I had been taught to understand the practice of Judaism in the worlds of church and theological college. For that reason, it took me a while to recognize that the beliefs and practices of the Biblical narrators were quite different to the belief and practice of mainstream Judaism at the grassroots.

In this same vein, the redactor of II Kings gives us a clear feeling for what C7th-C6thBCE Jewish believers thought and felt about Yahweh. It is not what I expected. They disparaged him. The New Jerusalem Bible says, *"They spoke slightingly of Yahweh their Powerful One."* They defamed him. They did not respect him. *"They rejected his decrees."* To spell it out, the mainstream Jewish memory of Yahweh at this point, in the C8th-6thBCE, was essentially negative. The regime of Yahweh's laws had largely been dispensed with. Yahweh was seen, in essence, as their former ruler, and good riddance. By contrast, as the people's devotional practices reveal, the mainstream Jewish memory of Asherah was positive. How is that possible, and why on Earth would that be?

From the time I entered the world of Christian faith, as a teenager, I was taught that Yahweh was the Jewish holy name for God, and that as such he was far above and beyond any court of public opinion. So, when I first allowed myself to read these Biblical passages slowly enough to recognize what the redactor is telling us regarding ancient Jewish opinion on Yahweh, I was truly dumbfounded. How could the Jewish people have a negative view of Yahweh? Wasn't it Yahweh who rescued their ancestors from slavery in Egypt? Wasn't it Yahweh who called his people into being as the descendants of Abraham and Sarah? Wasn't Yahweh the transcendent and perfect creator of the universe? If the ancient Hebrew people didn't see Yahweh that way, then how did they see him? If they did not think of Yahweh as God, then who or what exactly did they think he was? And why would their attitude towards Yahweh be negative, and their feelings towards Asherah be positive?

If I were to put these questions to most of my Bible-believing friends, I would expect to be met with looks of either total bemusement or grave offence. Surely, there is only one GOD and him Yahweh. Today, if you suggest that Yahweh may have originally been one half of a couple, male and female, you are likely to face a raised eyebrow or two. Offer this as teaching in a church and you are likely to be invited not to return! But as I follow the white rabbit of root meanings down and deep into the rabbit warren of Scripture, the picture that emerges clearly reveals that Yahweh was not alone. There was also Asherah, and she was not the only other deity in the Hebrew pantheon. Far from it. Yahweh and Asherah were only two of many.

30

When I arrived at this cliff-hanger of a conclusion in the quiet of my shipping crate cabin, I remember feeling a long way from home. This was far from the cozy world of conventional Christianity, which had reassured me with the image of an empty cosmos, presided over by a God with no competitors, whose rules I felt I had more or less got my head around. The world I was finding in this earlier layer of the Bible was something far messier. I instinctively knew this was also a world I could not discuss with almost all the friends and colleagues I had gathered through thirty-three years of church-based ministry. So many assumptions about God and the Bible have to be laid to one side to explore this territory, and I soon found that, beyond one or two senior colleagues, not many in my immediate circles were prepared to do that.

For these reasons, it was a great encouragement to me to find a fellow pilgrim in paleocontact whose *bona fides* in the world of Bible translation make him a voice to be listened to. To be honest, I didn't know who he was as I penned *Escaping from Eden*, my first offering in the world of paleocontact. Only as I finished up its final chapters did I first hear of a controversial Bible scholar in Italy who had reached conclusions very similar to my own, and who was making waves with his own books about Bible translation. He is, arguably, one of the most controversial Bible scholars in modern times. His work gives a context for why Yahweh and Asherah might turn out to have more peer-to-peer company than the Bible, as we have it, has cared to make clear. His friendship has encouraged me to continue in my research journey. Our conversation with this courageous scholar in the next chapter will have us questioning whether Almighty God shows up at all in the Bible we thought we knew. By the time our conversation ends we will have cause to question our assumptions not only about God and the Bible, but about life, the universe and everything!

Chapter Three

Coffee, Councils and Thought-Control

Rome 2022

I love the smell of the hot and humid breeze through the city's ancient stone squares and streets. I like the buzz of the Vespas, and the smell of their fumes. Blended with the hubbub of animated conversation and the warm, inviting aromas of fresh bread and good coffee, I feel very happy to be once again in the historic city of Rome. Even at night, the temperate climate invites people of every age out into the vistas and piazzas, to eat, drink, and enjoy the romance and nightlife of Rome.

As I drive with my family towards the Piazza di Spagna, my attention is caught by a female police officer. She is patrolling the streets to control the flow of traffic through an area full of pedestrians. From underneath her police cap hang superlong tresses of curly blonde hair, and as she walks across the cobbles towards the car in front of us, I can't help noticing her super-high heels, not stilettos, but close to. This is not how traffic police dress in England, where I grew up, nor in Australia, where I live today. Evidently, it is how they dress in Italy. Yet, however impractical her footwear may appear to be, this police officer is having no trouble stopping traffic!

There is so much to love about Rome. We are surrounded by the glories of the Colosseum, the Arcus Titi, the Pantheon, the Trevi Fountain, the Spanish Steps and the incredible Palatino. There is also much I love about Italian culture, the love of family, the love of beauty, the enthusiasm for fashion and style. I admire the vision for society reflected in many of Italy's public policies and in the fact that almost all my Italian friends are active political enthusiasts. Of course, there is a shadow side to this with the fractious and volatile dynamics of Italy's party-political life. The city of Rome itself has a shadow side too, and on this visit, more than on previous occasions, I am mindful of some of the darker, deeper streams of history which find their headwaters in this city. It was not so long ago, and not much more than half a mile due West of this pleasant cafe, that uniformed officers of the Church tied the renaissance scholar, Giordano Bruno to a stake, cut off his tongue and set him alight, burning him to death for promoting the theory that God may have populated the universe with other inhabited planets, and that on this planet we might educate ourselves to be more intelligent, accessing higher cognitive function through the use of ancient techniques and protocols. If you have ever wondered how the Catholic authorities of Rome persuaded a genius of the renaissance like Marsilio Vicino to close his university of sciences, or how it was they convinced Copernicus and Galileo to retract their pioneering science of the cosmos, or how they ensured that Galileo would not only renounce his scientific research but also resign himself to life under house arrest, you need to look no further than the public execution of Giordano Bruno for an answer. Controlling the minds of the masses has been big business in this city for a long time.

In my research for *Echoes of Eden* I learned that the letters patent which authorized the genocide of a million Cathars, living in the South of France in the 1200s were issued less than four miles from where we are sitting. Similarly, the papal licenses which gave Catholic Kings the warrant to slaughter thousands of Central and South American priests and their monarchs, and to incinerate the vast libraries of the historic cultures of Central and South America, were signed in this city. The mandates for violence and murder, issued to kings and mercenaries in order to effect the regime-change of country after country around the world, those licenses were signed and issued only four miles to the west of where we are sitting right now. And in case you are thinking that these historic exercises in thought control bear no relation to the modern world, that these are long-forgotten crimes relegated to the distant recesses of history, think again. My host for today's brunch can tell you otherwise. In fact, his very career is an object lesson revealing that the dynamics of religious thought-control in the twenty-first century are as alive as ever.

My friend Mauro Biglino is a real firebrand, a man whose outstanding work has probably offended as many good people as I have. Like Bruno, he is a scholar and a radical. Perhaps it is fitting that we will have today's conversation in a city which has been the arena for orthodoxy versus controversy for the best part of two thousand years. Mauro is an internationally bestselling author, known especially for his controversial book, *The Naked Bible*. A researcher and a highly regarded scholar of ancient Hebrew, he worked in Rome for many years for the *Edizioni San Paulo* as a Bible translator, providing with great precision the literal meaning of Hebrew words for Vatican-approved interlinear Bibles and supervising the translations for publication. Indeed, Mauro's supervision and finessing of the translation of the Pentateuch and the prophets major and minor was commended by the Senior Editor of the *Edizioni San Paolo,* as being meticulous. It was a public acknowledgment from an internationally respected scholarly team that Mauro's work had lifted theirs. This is a great complement from a highly regarded authority in the world of Bible translation. One important aspect of Mauro's influence on the publisher's approach, out of deference to the importance and uncertainty around the words, was to leave the key names and titles, conventionally translated as *"Lord"* or *"God,"* untranslated.

"My great satisfaction," he enthuses, *"is that in these volumes elohim remained elohim, ruach remained ruach, elyon remained*

35

elyon, and so forth. Also, Yahweh remained Yahweh and not 'l'Eterno' as it usually is in Italian translations. This was a source of great satisfaction for me because it was my argument. The conventional translations are inventions. My intention is always to be as respectful as possible towards the ancient authors and get an idea of what the Bible probably has to say beyond what theology has told us."

As Mauro recounts his story to me, I make a mental note of his wise approach of leaving enigmatic names and titles untranslated. As you will see in a few chapters, it is a tool which will come in handy for me in pastoral conversations at a later juncture, and in a country far away. And the words Mauro just listed? We will take a closer look at what secrets they may hold in the chapters ahead.

Mauro's chosen discipline was an exacting one, rigorous in avoiding any kind of spin or nuanced interpretation of a word, presenting only the basic, etymological meaning of each word or word part. This was the precise kind of work Mauro was born to do. Unfortunately, Mauro's meticulous discipline in translation would ultimately set him at odds with his publisher's major client. On the one hand the *Edizioni San Paulo* had a loyalty to the text, while on the other its chief client was the Vatican and the Roman Catholic Church at large. Mauro soon found that his own loyalty to the text was forcing a parting of ways. However, Mauro is eager for me to know that their parting was not in any way acrimonious.

"They kept my translations for the Pentateuch and the major and minor prophets, and they kept those key words untranslated in the way I had argued for. And as people our relationships were always warm and cordial."

It was simply a matter of *Edizioni San Paulo* providing for its major client and he who pays the piper calls the tune. This was not the first time Bible translators had to make choices influenced by their major client. *Edizioni San Paulo* navigated those dynamics with grace and subtlety. By contrast, in a later chapter we will see how their predecessors by twenty-six centuries found the need to make editorial decisions which would be far from subtle, redefining from that time to this our whole understanding of the Bible, ourselves as a species, and of the cosmos itself. Arguably, this was one of the most significant moments of thought control in history.

Since his time with *Edizioni San Paulo*, Mauro's continuing research has propelled him onto the international stage, where his work has opened up a world of cultural memory, recorded in the Bible, yet hidden from the public by editorial decisions now twenty-six centuries old. Mauro's efforts in translation of root meanings have provided a way for the public to view earlier layers of Biblical information, very different to the doctrines and dogmas associated with the Bible in its current form. So, you can see why he and I are friends! From early 2022, on the *Mauro Biglino Channel* and *The 5th Kind TV*, Mauro and I recorded a series of conversations together. In it we share our thoughts on the key Biblical words which have led each of us respectively into the world of paleocontact. The series garnered millions of online views and has filled our in-trays to overflowing with correspondence from people around the world who had long suspected the information our research has uncovered. Often, our correspondents have found themselves frozen out of fellowship in their church communities for having seen the implication of these ancient Hebrew words. In other cases, these mysteries have been responsible for introducing new readers to the world of the Bible. So, we are both delighted with the fruit of that research.

Today is the first time Mauro and I have met face to face, in the flesh, and it is a real pleasure for me to sit down with Mauro, eat and drink together, and compare notes on all the issues of the day – including our respective areas of research. Mauro refers me to another Italian scholar with a fascination for Hebrew language.

"Joseph Garbini was professor of Semitic Philology at the Sapienza University of Rome. He argued that Hebrew is in fact a Canaanite dialect, one of many. Today we only know Hebrew as it was reconstructed at the end of the first millennium after Christ, what is called Masoretic Hebrew."

"You will have noticed that when we read the Bible in the Hebrew we do not read a text bound by grammatical rules. Rather the texts follow an ideological path. Grammatical rules were not a problem for the authors. Grammar was not the master."

This was something I had noticed for myself in my years as a lecturer in hermeneutics. For example, the oldest word used in the Bible which translators render as God is the Hebrew word *elohim*. What is curious is that, though often translated in the singular, it is not a singular word form. It has the form of a masculine plural. I had noticed the odd grammatical phenomena surrounding the word. I could see that the word *elohim* is often accompanied by plural form verbs, and that it exhibits plural behaviours such as conversations, competition, conflict, and even wars. It was the plural verb forms and attributives in the Bible's elohim texts which first clued me that in the beginning these texts were not about GOD, rather they were about a plurality of entities. Even in various moments where a post-Moses redactor had superimposed the name Yahweh over the original vocabulary of elohim, the plural verb forms would sometimes remain. Through my research for *Escaping from Eden* I came to see that these grammatical glitches were in reality the crease marks created by the C6thBCE redactors when they reworked texts about multiple elohim in an attempt to morph them into texts about a single deity. Or to put it another way, these grammatical glitches were the scar tissue left by the surgery that changed the Bible from a library of paleocontact into a book about God. (If you're not yet convinced, my book *Escaping from Eden* shows my working and lays out the logic for this conclusion.)

Mauro continues. *"Even Jewish exegetes say that in the Hebrew language there is no term that indicates 'God' as we understand it. There is no word that indicates an omniscient, omnipotent, transcendent spiritual entity."*

This fact might come as a surprise to a lot of believers because for centuries we have been taught to believe that the Bible is all about an omniscient, omnipotent, transcendent, spiritual God. To learn that the Bible doesn't even have a word for that concept comes as quite a shock. The real scandal is that this information is known among senior, academic Jewish exegetes and to an any serious scholar of the vocabulary of the Bible – which should include every priest and pastor. The problem is that, overscheduled as most congregational pastors are, and dependent as most pastors are on the goodwill of their congregations, few of us have the freedom and luxury to follow the white rabbit of that little gem of information to its logical conclusion.

The oldest word in the Bible that gets translated as *God* is *elohim*. The great secret is not only that the masculine plural form of the word indicates a plurality of beings, but that it represents a wide diversity of beings, some good and some not so much. The root meaning of the word is the *Powerful Ones*. In that light, perhaps the Bible should be reframed not as *"God's book"* but as *"The Book About the Wide Range of Powerful Ones, Good and Bad."* Admittedly, this is a less snappy title, but it may be more apt to the original meanings of the texts.

In various Bible translations elohim is also translated as judges, legislators, governors, the bright ones from above, and some other words, which indicated the functions that these beings performed but without saying who they really were. One example of this uncertainty comes in the story of Abraham and Sarah, the progenitors of the Hebrew tradition. When Abraham and Sarah left the home of their birth in Ur of the Chaldes, they brought with them all the stories of beginnings with which they would have grown up. These were the Mesopotamian stories of Sky People, beings from the stars with names like *Enlil*, the Space Commander, *Enki* the Earth Commander, *Namma*, the primordial mother, *Ninhursag* the primordial nurse, and *Qingu* the involuntary donor whose DNA helped to genetically modify the first humans. These were powerful ones indeed.

The Sky People were advanced in all kinds of ways, and the memory of them is etched into the more than half a million cuneiform tablets, recording the culture which formed the worldview of Abraham and Sarah. In Genesis 20:13 Abraham is asked by his Canaanite host why he had decided to move from Ur of the Chaldes and embark on such a major transmigration with all his retinue, livestock and possessions. Abraham's answer: *"The powerful ones* (the plural root meaning of *elohim*) *told* (plural verb form) *me to."*

Abraham does not specify who or what these plural Powerful Ones were. Only that they (plural) told him to leave, and that he had either followed their advice, or had not had the liberty to disagree. Of course, I have received plenty of correspondence from believers struggling to come to terms with this information. Some are very assertive that the equation of *elohim* with God is a fundamental truth of Biblical translation. Mauro's in tray has been graced with similar contributions. I ask Mauro how he generally responds.

40

"I find that to show the true perspective it is sufficient, for example, to take Psalm 82 which clearly speaks of an assembly of the elohim."

This makes sense. The answers are in the texts. I recall that my own discovery in the Bible of the *El Ba'adat (Council of Power)* was a worldview-shifting moment. To realise that project Earth has been governed over by a federation of beings as diverse as the crowd in the famous Star Wars bar scene, blew away my former worldview of an empty universe populated intelligently only by God and human beings. Even more shocking for me was to learn that the entity in the Bible which I had taken for God turns out to be no more a junior member of that council. But that is for a later chapter!

In my *Eden* books to date, *Escaping from Eden, The Scars of Eden,* and *Echoes of Eden,* I argue that the Bible's Sky Council and elohim stories make better sense if we read them with the original Hebrew words still in place or if we use a root meaning as a way of peeling back centuries of cultural interpretation. When we do this the stories change, but not in a random way. They change in a way that resolves many of the moral questions relating to the behaviour of the elohim, why their actions are often so brutal, anti-human and unconscionable. Understanding that we are reading stories which are not about God, but about a spectrum of extra-terrestrial invaders and visitors clarifies how it is that thousands of human beings get slaughtered in the conflict of the elohim - something which makes no sense with elohim mistranslated in the singular as *God*.

Another significant fact emerges from reading *elohim* as the *Powerful Ones*. The moment we make that switch, it becomes clear that we are reading the summary form of the source narratives from out of ancient Mesopotamia, the narratives of Sumeria, Babylonia, Akkadia and Assyria. More than a hundred

41

and fifty years after the translation of the Mespotamian cuneiform texts revealed this relationship, many Biblical scholars are still struggling with the implications, and most of the rank and file of our churches and synagogues have no idea about it.

The theologian Michael Heiser is one scholar who has been willing to name the presence and diversity of the elohim and shine a light on the parallels between the Biblical texts and their Mesopotamian sources. However, in the hope of maintaining a sufficient number of the shibboleths of Christian orthodoxy, Michael proposes that what the Biblical writers have done is take the Mesopotamian stories and *"invert"* them, turning them on their heads to tell a different story. The problem with his argument is that the Biblical version does not tell a different story. It tells the same story, only in summary form.

For instance, both Sumerian and Biblical texts speak about winds terraforming a flooded world, separating the waters, saltwater from freshwater, and reclaiming dry land for the development of animal and human life. In the Sumerian story the creative agent is the four winds. In the Bible it is the ruach, a word which at root means *wind*. Same story. No inversion.

For another example, in the Sumerian story there is a conflict among the Sky People over whether the humans should be male and female, fertile, conscious, and intelligent. Enlil the senior, the Space Commander, says no. *"We don't want them too much like us."* Enki, (an older brother though junior in rank) breaks rank and proceeds unilaterally with the genetic modification to upgrade the humans. As the natural consequence of their upgrade, the humans begin pairing off and, as time progresses, the human population on Earth multiplies to the point that the Sky Council begins to feel both annoyed and threatened by the growth in number and advancement of human beings. Their initial counter-measure is to limit the lifespans of the now fertile human beings. When this fails to appease his concerns, Enlil pushes a decision through the council to cull the human population by means of a massive, genocidal flood.

In the Bible, precisely the same story is told in Genesis chapters 3-6, but with Yahweh in the role of the senior player opposed to human progress. In Genesis 3 it is Yahweh who wishes human beings to remain at an animal level, so unintelligent they don't even know their naked. It is Yahweh who speaks the words of Enlil, *"No we don't want them too much like us."* (There's that plural again!) It is Yahweh who limits human lifespans and Yahweh who sends the genocidal flood. And it is the Serpent, representing Enki, who upgrades the human beings for a better and happier human experience. This is not an inversion. It's the same story.

I completely agree with what Mauro told me in Rome, namely that when the final redaction of the Hebrew Canon was done in the C7th-C6th BCE the driving agenda was an ideological one, not a grammatical one. That ideology was monotheism, and the intent of the redactors was to erase every memory of this vast panoply of ancient visitors. However, our ancient visitors are not so easy to airbrush out of the picture.

- In the book of Job, we read of Behemoth and Leviathan which are fearful beasts, with which Yahweh compares himself
- In various places we have Seraphim or Serpents, fearsome dragon-like entities. In fact, the Bible use the words *serpent* and *dragon* interchangeably.
- In the book of Leviticus, we read of Moloch offerings. These child-sacrifices are condemned by the narrators. But who or what were the child victims being offered to?

43

- In Genesis 6, the *Benei Elohim* (the *Watchers* of the Book of Enoch and the *gods* of Greek and Norse legend) play a diverse role, on the one hand nurturing and tutoring ancient humans, and on the other hand abducting human females for hybridization.
- Throughout the Bible we have Baal, generally mentioned in the context of competition for resources and hegemony. Who or what is he?
- In II Kings we have the scenario of separate human colonies, governed over by competing *elohim*. The text reveals a bitter rivalry between Yahweh and the neighboring Elohim of Ekron. Indeed, it is Yahweh who refers to himself and his neighbour both as *elohim*.
- In I Kings 22 we have a glimpse of the machinations of the Sky Council, noting that one of its members is described as a *"spirit."* In ancient times this word did not necessarily mean an immaterial or energy-based being. Rather it implied a being which could *"spirit itself"* instantly from one location to another and disappear without leaving a trail. (We will come back to this fascinating word in a later chapter.)
- In a more pleasant vein, we are told about the plural visitors to Jacob in Genesis. These are beings which arrive on Earth and disappear back up into the sky via a mystifying form of technology, which the narrator describes as a *"ladder."*
- And finally, we have Asherah, the nurturer of human civilization, and the mother of farming.

Whether you take these narratives as memories or fictions, what is unarguable is that they are narratives of a very wide range of elohim.

By the time my months of research had brought me to these conclusions I had been a preacher for thirty-three years. For a long time, I felt I had been scratching only the surface of the Bible's ancient texts. When I set out to drill down into the anomalies which had pointed me to a deeper, older layer of story in the pages of the good book, I expected to find some exciting, buried treasure to enhance my preaching. I did not expect this.

In one sense I could embrace Michael Heiser's language of *"inversion"* to describe the new story emerging from the root meanings of these ancient words. But it was not that the Bible was an inversion of the Mesopotamian stories of paleocontact and genetic engineering. Rather many of the God stories we have told from the Bible for more than two millennia are, in reality, an inversion of the original meaning of the Biblical texts.

I realized that in order to be honest to the original meanings I had to concede that the Biblical stories were telling me about a time when our planet was colonized by visitors from space, some of whom nurtured our emergence as a species and a civilization, and others of whom ruled over us, waged wars with us, genetically engineered and modified us, dominated and enslaved us, counting us as collateral damage in their conflicts over the progress of project Earth. This was a far less reassuring image of the universe, compared to my formerly orthodox view of a cosmos, completely empty of advanced sentient life, save for humanity and our familiar transcendent God. On the other hand, the picture of cosmic neighbours emerging in the Biblical texts was more reassuring than much of today's popular storytelling concerning cosmic neighbours. Today the word *extraterrestrial* or *alien* evokes visions of *Mars Attacks, Invasion of the Body Snatchers, Independence Day, War of the Worlds,* or Ridley Scott's *Alien* franchise. As we have already seen the paleocontact stories curated by the world's indigenous cultures, including those of the Bible and their Mesopotamian sources, are far more layered.

In the Sumerian narratives we hear of many Sky People by name, and they play different kinds of roles in the human story. Enlil (male) the commander of this region of space, is the commander in chief, the conqueror and colonizer. It is he who lays down the law and presides over the Sky Council. His older brother Enki (male) is the genetic engineer and upgrader of humanity. Qingu (male) is our Sky People ancestor. He is a defeated warrior whose blood is extracted and used to engineer the first human beings. The Sky People wanted a homo sapiens similar enough to their masters to be a compatible work force, yet vulnerable enough to be easily dominated. Hence the defeated Qingu appeared to Enlil and Enki to be the ideal candidate for a DNA donation to modify our primate ancestors. Surely his human descendants would be advanced and yet easily dominated! Unmistakably, there is a negative timbre in the male side of the Sky People story as they intersected with the development of our ancestors. They are stories of our being controlled and corralled. Though Enki appears to be a friend and supporter of humanity, he is sandwiched between the dominating Enlil and the defeated Qingu. The accounts of our ancestors' colonization and adaptation by this conquering force leave a funny taste in the mouth.

The Sky People narratives also speak of female entities: Ninhursag (female) is the primordial nurse, nurturing the developing human beings as we change from animal Earthlings to an upgraded homo sapiens sapiens. Namma (female) is the original *"Mama"*, the mother of creation, the mother of the Sky People and nurturer of Earth. In the Epic of Gilgamesh, we are introduced to Shamhat (female) who tutors the primate human Enkidu. She introduces the primitive man to more developed foods and drinks and prepares him for city living. This aspect of

46

our ancient contact carries more positive associations. The female characters appear to represent a cultural memory of cosmic contact which was affirming and supportive rather than dominating and controlling.

Immersed in the world of the Mesopotamian Sky People, I begin to join the dots and see how the Sky People narratives reflect in the Biblical stories of the Powerful Ones, and I find a different light cast upon the experiences of our Hebrew ancestors. Back in Tel Arad in chapter two we were left perplexed and wondering how it was that in the Judaism of C8th-6thBCE the people's associations around Yahweh were negative and around Asherah were positive. The answer is there to be found once we realize that the Bible's sources comprise a spectrum of paleocontact experiences, some positive and some negative. According to Mesopotamian memory, the negative aspect of colonization and control, demonstrating power, exercising authority and laying down the law are all associated with the male side of the equation in the characters of Enlil, Enki and Qingu. Meanwhile, the positive aspect of visitors who nurtured and supported our ancestors' development, tutoring us as far as city-building, is associated with the female side of the Mesopotamian story, represented in the characters of Namma, Ninhursag, and Shamhat.

These two poles of paleocontact are there too in the Bible's summaries of these stories. The male aspect is characterized in Yahweh and the female in Asherah. Yahweh, representing the male aspect, is the powerful colonizer, ruthlessly conquering, ruling with authority and laying down the law. Asherah, the female aspect, is the mother-figure, the life-giver and nurturer, who raises humanity to farm-making, community-building, and city-living. Seen against that background, the freeze-frame offered by II Kings 17, which depicted the Jewish people's rejection of Yahweh and their affection for Asherah, begins to make more sense. In a fuller light we can understand the engravings of Yahweh and Asherah side by side as a reference to the full spectrum of paleocontact experiences, with Yahweh and Asherah representing the two poles in that wide range of cultural memory.

The implications for humanity of those two respective poles offer quite a contrast. The male side of the paleocontact story, represented by Yahweh, presents us as a species brought into existence purely to slave for Yahweh. In this Yahwist world obedience is counted as virtue. Wisdom is to fear Yahweh and to surrender our own mind to the mind of the Powerful One. The purpose of life is to sublimate our will to the will of Yahweh, because we exist purely for the Powerful One's purposes and pleasure. This all sounds very close to mainstream Jewish and Christian views of God which have flowed from the Bible's Yahweh narratives.

By contrast, the female side of the story offers a different view of humanity. According to the actions of Asherah, human beings are incredibly valuable. She meets humanity in our moment of need and vulnerability, and shares her deep knowledge with us, to equip us to build civilizations of our own. To Asherah we are worth nurture and intimate connection because there is something uniquely valuable about who we are as a species. Alongside each other, the two strands of story reflect a spectrum of contact experiences through the ages. To lose the female side of the equation, not only distorts the picture of our cosmic company, but it also distorts how we think of ourselves as a species.

Are we valuable or are we chattels? Are we something unique and beautiful? Or are we no more than unworthy servants for our powerful masters and those who rule on their behalf? In this sense, losing the female side of the story carries profound implications for our psychology as a species. Sadly, it is the female aspect of the story which found itself marginalized, distorted and, as best as possible, airbrushed out. Through a quite deliberate process, the Bible changed from being a book which portrayed Yahweh, Asherah and many others besides, into a book with an empty cosmos and a solo God called Yahweh. How exactly that happened, why it happened and who initiated it is an array of questions to which we will return in a later chapter. But first I have to reply to a correspondent who has written to me insisting that the authors of the Bible got it right when they made these editorial calls. He has written me several long paragraphs intended to persuade me that the Biblical authors were inspired by the Spirit of God to write what they did, and that furthermore they did the right thing by editing out this other layer of story. Perhaps, he says, we should just trust the Biblical writers' judgement call that Asherah was no more than a silly story and was really not relevant to the inspired monotheism of Judaism. Asherah was an unhelpful distraction, a religious side-show, unworthy of serious attention from enlightened, educated people like you and me. Is he right? Could that be true?

To answer that question, we need to step out of the world of ancient literature and get our feet on the ground in the sticks-and-stones, blood-and-bones world of archaeology and real-world history. Let's get our hands on some solid, material objects to fill out our picture of just what it was our ancestors were seeing. To do that we will need to leave Rome and head to a different part of the world where we will travel into the mountainous terrain of modern-day Palestine. There a find of physical artefacts will provide us with a window onto humanity's past, the most mind-blowing of all carved into a solid piece of stone twelve inches tall.

Chapter Four

A Doll and a Doorway

Tel El-Farah - 7 miles northeast of Nablus, Palestine

We are on a windswept, stony plateau, high in the rugged mountain country of Samaria. This expanse of forty-five acres has been an archeological site since the 1940s, when Roland de Vaux, director of the École Biblique et Archéologique Française, initiated a major excavation. Across the Levant, sites like this one provide us with an amazing window onto the world of the Bible through a body of physical artefacts, buildings, decorations, carvings, ornaments, jewelry, and figurines. They may not be direct physical representations in the photographic sense, but they do give us eyes on what our Hebrew ancestors were seeing, thinking, and imagining, when they spoke of Yahweh, Asherah and other powerful beings from the deep past. What was found here at Tel El-Farah in the twentieth century takes us even further than that.

Among the archeological finds made here was an extraordinary carving which has left us a clue as to who Asherah was and where she came from. Similar archeological finds across the region give us a very clear picture of just how widespread devotion to Asherah really was. For instance, the clay Asherah figurines, which we encountered in great numbers at the Tel Arad harvest festival, can be found in the remains of iron age homes scattered throughout the landscape of ancient Judea. This physical evidence reveals that these figurines were a standard item in Jewish family homes at that time. Asherah's place in Jewish family ritual was unmistakably mainstream. Across the region, the depictions of Asherah are countless. In fact, among all the symbols of Jewish decoration, notwithstanding the Second Commandment not to depict *"other powerful ones,"* Asherah is by far the most popular. Always we find her portrayed with the authority and dignity befitting a great and powerful being. Sometimes she takes the physical form of a woman accompanied by symbols of life, and fertility. Often, she can be recognized by her bouffant hair. Sometimes she is bare-breasted, and other times she takes the form of a verdant tree, usually an olive tree. At Taanach we see Asherah portrayed as the Lion Lady.

To put this visual reference to the Lion Lady in a near-contemporary context, you may be familiar with the famous image of Gilgamesh, King of Uruk in what is now Iraq Gilgamesh was, according to Sumerian accounts, a powerful hybrid king, part human and part Sky People. He is the hero of the world's oldest novel, the famous *Epic of Gilgamesh*. Taken from the Palace of Sargon at Khorsabad, in northern Iraq, this ancient carving of Gilgamesh dating from the C8thBCE now adorns the Assyrian collection in the Louvre in Paris. It is enormous, standing at more than sixteen feet tall (5 meters.) The size and power of Gilgamesh are represented by the fact that he is standing, easily holding in one arm a full-grown male lion. The relative sizes, in which the adult lion looks like a domestic lap cat, reveal that Gilgamesh was huge. But whereas the Assyrians of ancient Iraq portrayed Gilgamesh carrying one lion, the artists who carved the Lion Lady at Taanach depict a naked Asherah holding two lions, by the ears. This is female power and no mistake! Loving nurturer of humanity she may be, but the Lion Lady is evidently not to be messed with.

Back in Tel Arad, our narrator at the harvest festival was correct in pointing out the great number of temples and Asherah installations across the country. King Manasseh of Judah is noted in II Kings 21 for installing an image of Asherah in the Jerusalem

Temple. And why wouldn't he if nobody less than King Solomon, the high point of the Jewish monarchy, had seen fit to construct an entire temple in honour of Asherah to the east of Jerusalem. (II Kings 23:13) Similarly King Jeroboam of Israel had a temple built for Asherah at Bethel, the place where Jacob had erected standing stones to commemorate his close encounters in that place.

Close to Jerusalem, bronze arrow heads have been found bearing the inscription: *"A son of Anat and servant of the Lion Lady."* In two places inscriptions have been found, naming Yahweh and Asherah, side by side, as peer-to-peer figures in the Jewish pantheon. At Khirbet el Qom near Hebron, a burial inscription was unearthed which dates from the C8thBCE. It reads: *"Blessed be Uriah by Yahweh and his Asherah. For he has saved him from his enemies."* In 1975 at Kuntillet 'Ajrud in the Sinai desert, a pottery shard from a storage jar was found with this message engraved into it: *"I have blessed you by Yahweh of Samaria and his Asherah."* Surely Yahweh and Asherah can't have been an item?

Some theologians have tried to suggest that the words *"Yahweh's Asherah"* could refer to an Asherah pole, a clay figurine, or some other Asherah related item. This explanation fails on several counts. Firstly, what sense would it make to speak a blessing in the name of Yahweh plus an accessory. The most prolific representations of *"an Asherah"* in iron age Jewish practice were the hand-held clay dolls. How likely does it sound to you that a blessing would be invoked in the name of Yahweh and his doll? Furthermore, if Asherah accessories were being condemned by Yahweh's prophets, which they were, it would be nonsensical for Yahweh to be known for his possession of one.

Another reason we have to accept that Asherah was more than a physical emblem is the role and function of Asherah's prophets. I Kings 18:19 references 400 spokespeople or messengers for

Asherah. Again, the suggestion here is that even in a world of Asherah accessories, figurines and poles, prophets are presenting themselves as mediating messages from an intelligent entity. The moment we survey other ancient literature from the region it becomes very clear that Asherah, otherwise known as Elat, Anat, Ashrat, Astarte, Qudshu, Hathor, Asherah of the Sea, the Lion Lady, and the mother of the gods, was understood to be a powerful entity. The more logical explanation of these inscriptions referencing *"Yahweh and his Asherah"* is that until the liturgical reforms of the C7thCE, Yahweh (male) and Asherah (female) were both regarded as powerful entities whose favour a person would do well to enjoy.

Our narrator at Tel Arad wondered if the memory of Asherah could really be airbrushed from history. Ultimately, the answer is, *"Not entirely."* Indeed, the memory of our ancestors' contact with this powerful female tutor can be found in the art and literature of countries well beyond Judea. We find her in Egypt, depicted in the tomb of Thutmosis III. The ancient Greek pantheon has re-imagined her as Aphrodite, and in ancient Rome they call her Venus. Travel through Greece and Cyprus and in every eastern orthodox church where an olive tree graces the courtyard, adorned with evidence of prayers and offerings, what you are looking at is the continued veneration of Asherah.

The texts and archeological artefacts we have just surveyed reveal the attachment of ancient Judaism to narratives of paleocontact and the wide spread of devotion to ancient helpers like Asherah. II Kings 17 reminds us of what was evidently a mainstream distaste for Yahwist religion and law, with its civic and religious powers centered on the King at Jerusalem and the High Priest of the Jerusalem Temple. The strength of those prior paleocontact traditions is evidenced in the fact that to effect this *"clean up"* of religious practice and ritual, King Josiah had to send the army in.

Every vestige of a polytheistic or henotheistic worldview had to be forcibly removed from Jewish practice. As a strict monotheist, Josiah believed in only one God – the God of the Jews, whose name was Yahweh. His kingdom was to be a theocracy with one God, one High Priest and one God-given King. This was Josiah's vision of a devout theocratic society with him as God's vice-regent.

Another part of the machinery for managing the religious experiences of the people at large was the illegalization of substances used by their shamanic ancestors to facilitate spiritual encounter experiences through altered states of consciousness. The knowledge of these modalities is embedded in the activities of the priestly caste and some of the Hebrew prophets. (I elaborate further on this aspect of Jewish high priestcraft in my book *Echoes of Eden.*) But now, under the theocratic reign of King Josiah, on the basis of Yahwhist law, the shamanic oil and smoke protocols for mystical experiences of contact and communication were strictly reserved for members of the Jerusalem priestly caste who were allowed access to the inner sanctuary of the Jerusalem temple. For anyone else they were simply illegal. This is why in the Biblical texts we see enforcers for Josiah and the High Priest dispatching armies throughout the kingdom to demolish the many temples of old Judaism, knocking down their standing stones, and desecrating their divining rooms. It is why the royal and religious militia prosecuted a campaign of confiscating, breaking and defacing images of Asherah, Baal, and any object of devotion directed to any figure other than Yahweh.

Against this background we can see that the narrator who shared the harvest festival with us at Tel Arad was in fact a typical devout Jew of the C8th-C7th BCE. He attended his local temple, gave reverence to the local standing stones, and thereby honoured the memory of ancient visits from advanced non-human beings. This is what Judaism was before the forcible processes of monotheization under the rule of kings Hezekiah and Josiah.

What King Josiah did in the C7thBCE to reform Jewish ritual and practice was taken to the next level in the C6thBCE with a parallel reform of the Hebrew Scriptures. This reform was undertaken by scribes selected by the High Priestly family of the Jerusalem Temple. The goal of this textual clean-up was to airbrush from the earlier versions of the Biblical texts, any vestiges of veneration of Asherah, or Baal or of any entity other than Yahweh. The order of the day was to rework the kaleidoscopic Hebrew canon into a harmonious whole, teaching monotheism from beginning to end.

You may think I have really stuck my neck out in saying this. However, although it might come as a surprise to many people of faith, nothing in what I just said is at all controversial in academic circles. In fact, there is a very wide scholarly consensus that the Bible took its current form, in this way, during the course of the C6thBCE. Its most ancient of narratives were the stories of beginnings, the elohim stories associated with Abraham and Sarah. They were the summary form of the Sky People narratives from out of ancient Sumeria, Akkadia, Babylonia and Assyria. (You can read about some of their most interesting parallels in my books *Escaping from Eden* and *The Scars of Eden.*)

Later, the books of Moses were produced to authenticate the lore and laws of Yahweh. This new Yahwist canon absorbed the earlier canon of Abrahamic elohim stories. This collection of scriptures was then pressed down and shaken together to create the *Pentateuch*, otherwise known as the *Torah*, and these first five books of the Bible emerged as a unified work at some point during the C7th and C6th BCE.

By the end of that same period other books had appeared, a fusion of national history and law. Their purpose was to authenticate the

Davidic monarchy and the Levitical priesthood and legitimize royal and high priestly authority as being divinely instituted. Known today as the Deuteronomistic History, it had taken its place in Judaism by some point in the C6thBCE. Then, at some point during the C6thBCE, the books of the *Nevi'im*, the major and minor prophets, were added to complete what we now call the Hebrew Canon. That's the consensus.

In this way the primitive form of Hebrew Canon emerged as a veritable kaleidoscope of ancient cultural memory, Yahwist laws and Yahwist stories, prophetic and poetic literature, summaries of Mesopotamian narratives, ancient liturgy, songs of praise, and cultural memories of contact with ancient helpers. Seen through the lens of King Josiah's vision of Yahweh as the one and only God, the kaleidoscope of sources in their original forms was a smorgasbord in need of a serious edit. The problem? It was too kaleidoscopic, the biggest issue being that it gave the appearance of having *"too many gods"* in it. The revision of the texts was the logical extension of Josiah's ritual reforms, driven by a religious ideology of monotheism. In the ideology of the redactors there was no place for even a hint of henotheism, polytheism or paleocontact. For the C6thBCE redactors, these were nothing other than *"idolatry."*

If you're not familiar with those other labels, polytheism is a devotion to many gods. Henotheism acknowledges many gods but serves only one. For instance, the moment when Joshua calls on the people of Israel to reject the powerful ones of Abraham, Sarah and their ancestors in Mesopotamia, and to cut off the powerful ones of the Amorites and Egyptians, and to serve only Yahweh, that is a vestige of a henotheistic Judaism. There are many powerful beings, but you work for this one.

Similarly, the Ten Commandments given to Moses are also the vestige of henotheistic Judaism. *"Have no other elohim before me,"* says Yahweh. *"Don't bow down to them. Don't even depict them."* Moments like these are the remnants of the world of what I would describe as *The Bible Before God*. The original shape of the old stories remains traceable in many places in the Bible as we now have it. However, the intention of the redactors was to harmonize what had been a smorgasbord and replace its kaleidoscopic vision with a strict Yahwist orthodoxy. The result of this revision was the Hebrew Canon as we now know it, *The Bible of One God, and him YHWH*. In this way, the dual reformation of ritual and scripture, took what people understood Judaism to be and changed it almost beyond recognition.

This is why the forty references to Asherah in the Bible as we now have it frame Asherah in a largely negative light. To turn *The Bible before God* into *The Bible of One God, and him YHWH*, we can see that the redactors and their Bible-translating successors have done three things to quietly airbrush the memory of Asherah out of the picture:

Firstly, in each instance when a Jewish King erects standing stones, installs high places, or constructs temples to Asherah, or commissions statues of her, the redactor adds a narrator's gloss, laced with value-laden language, in the style of the classic British satire, *"1066 and All That."* The redactor peppers his reports with phrases like *"King So and So was a Bad King, and what he did was a Very Bad Thing."* Or *"This was one of the many deplorable and atrocious things that King So and So did, which was really a predictable throwback to what his deplorable and atrocious ancestors did, who were just as bad as him, if not worse."*

However, what the redactor does not airbrush out is the bald fact that it was Hebrew Kings who built the altars to Baal and Asherah, and others. These were their choices. Could the redactor really claim to be wiser than Solomon? After all, the kings Manasseh, Ahab, Jeroboam and Solomon, all built temples to

Asherah. Every one of them commissioned the carving of statues in memory of Asherah and other entities. Like their ancestor Israel, otherwise known as Jacob, they too erected standing stones to mark where their people had first encountered these other beings, and they celebrated festivals to commemorate those moments of ancient contact. How could their noble kings be so wrong? The clever fix the redactors finally landed on is something I will return to a little later.

The second way the Bible, downplays the importance of these other Jewish temples is by translating them as *"high places,"* without ever really clarifying what a high place is. A temple or high place was a megalithic structure, built to house several altars, shrines and divining rooms. Each would be staffed by a cadre of priests. They would create and be supported by local economies. Support industries sprang up to provide accommodation, food, animals for offerings, crafting devotional objects like engravings of thanks to the Lion Lady, or manufacturing the clay figurines of Asherah to take home for household devotions.

Our Bibles give the impression to the casual reader that there was only ever one temple, *The Temple* in Jerusalem, under the curation of the High Priestly family. In reality the plurality of temples throughout Judea represented a powerful economic engine and were a significant agency in moving people and money around the country. For those reasons, the monopolizing of Judaism and the centralization of its powers to the Jerusalem Court and the Jerusalem Temple would have carried enormous financial and political implications for the towns and communities associated with all the other temples, and of course for the power and wealth of Jerusalem. Though they were all done in the name of routing out idolatry, the reforms of Jewish ritual and the redaction of the Hebrew scriptures which followed were at the same time an exercise in centralizing power and wealth.

59

The third way in which the profile of Asherah has been diminished is in the use of the expression *"an Asherah"* to refer to anything Asherah-related, ranging from a hand-held figurine to huge carved wooden installations in temples dedicated to her memory. By referring to them all as *"an Asherah"* it reduces Asherah to an object, and the powerful entity referenced by the object somehow gets forgotten. In the minds of the readers *"an Asherah"* was no more than a type of idol. Later translators have compounded this impression through the liberal use of the translation *"Asherah Pole"* to reference the numerous Asherah installations throughout Judea and beyond. The phrase *"Asherah pole"* conjures up an image of a redundant and unnecessary stick. In most places the text simply references *"an Asherah."* But whether represented by a doll, a pole, a statue, or a temple, Asherah, was remembered throughout the Levant with thanksgiving, and this meant festivals with food, drink, incense, and celebration.

The current redaction of the Hebrew Canon frames this wide spread of celebration in an entirely negative light and reports with enthusiasm all the activity of the royal and high priestly soldiers as they go around desecrating the hard copy of Judaism's recollection of paleocontact. The fact that this desecration was even needed, along with the continual refrain of the prophets, chastising people for commemorating Asherah and others, serves as a clear reminder of just how ubiquitous the memory of Asherah really was at the time of that final edit.

For all the honour she enjoyed, Asherah was clearly only one of a number of Powerful Ones referred to in the Hebrew canon. A reference to this wider context appears in *II Kings 23:4. "The king [Josiah] ordered Hilkiah the High Priest, the priests next in rank, and the gatekeepers, to remove from the temple of Yahweh all the items made for Baal and Asherah, along with all the Sky Armies."*

Now what does a *Sky Army* suggest to you? How do you picture that? Do you imagine a crowd of winged, white-sheet-wearing, naked people, rippling with muscles, Michelangelo-style, sitting astride fluffy white clouds, adorning a bright blue sky? Or do *Sky Armies* evoke an arsenal of technology, a powerful and menacing fleet replete with aircraft, space shuttles and mother ships, similar to the array of Vimanas described in clear and technological terms in the Vedas of ancient India? By contrast to the Vedic traditions of Hinduism, in the West we don't expect to find technology in our scriptures. We have become habituated to seeing the Biblical language of *Sky Army* and viewing it through a religious lens, the lens of Michelangelo and the Sistine chapel. Accordingly, the culturally familiar rendering in English of the Hebrew *seba hassamayim* is *heavenly host*. It conjures up images of a white-robed angelic choir, applauding and joining in our praises.

However, at root, the word *seba* (pr. *tzeva*) means *army* and *hassamayim* means *sky*. In many places the Bible uses the words in exactly that way. For instance, various Biblical texts refer to *uveof hassamayim,* the birds of the sky, to specify birds that are airborne, birds that can fly. *Seba hassamayim* can therefore be taken to mean armed forces that are airborne, a flying army. Ancient Judaism recognized the *seba hassmayim* as a cadre of powerful beings, which included Baal and Asherah. The attitude of ancient Judaism towards *"the whole Sky Army"* was one of veneration. This pantheon of powerful visitors in the deep past was remembered with awe and there was no sense of apology for describing the entities their ancestors saw.

The *Seba Hassamyim* appears in the Biblical narratives from out of the blue, so to speak. But where did they originate? Some cultures around the world are very specific about where our ancient visitors came from. The name suggests that they were from what today we would call *"outer space,"* from some place elsewhere in the Cosmos. In the Bible's source narratives, the Sumerian word *anunnaki,* indicated by a glyph representing the sky, makes this very same connection. Aboriginal Australian story, along with Cherokee story is more specific and goes so far as to name the region of space from which their cosmic tutors came. Their oral traditions name the Pleiades. The Dogon people of Mali, West Africa, name the Sirius star system. Ancient Egyptian lore points to Orion. The book of Job identifies all three regions of space in a single verse, in which the writer reflects a pattern of human subjection to powers from among those three specific constellations. (You will find this verse in Job 38.) So where is Asherah in this picture? Where does she belong in the heavenly array?

Ancient Jewish memory is carried in oral tradition, rituals, texts, and archaeology. And it is in archaeology that Jewish memory offers a hint as to where in the heavens Asherah may have originated. That's why we are interested in the excavations made by Roland de Vaux here at Tel El-Farah. One of the most important discoveries here revealed that this ancient city was home to a three-meter-high standing stone. The presence of this standing stone suggests that just like Bethel, with the standing stones installed by the patriarch Jacob, Tel El-Farah was itself a place of paleocontact.

Among the artefacts recovered from this site are evidences of other devotional practices dedicated to a local memory of paleocontact. Figurines of women carrying bread cakes make clear that Tel- El-Farah was a place of devotion to Asherah. But there is one Asherah-related item recovered from the site, which stands out from others for its cosmic significance. It is an object dating from the C10thBCE and it offers us an insight into how the Queen of Heaven might have appeared to the ancestors of the people at Tel El-Farah, and from where. This incredible object is a stone carving no more than twelve inches in length (30cm.) In the carved design, Asherah appears, represented by two inverted palm trees which frame some kind of a doorway. The doorway is flanked on either side by an inverted palm tree. Curiously, there is no building of any kind around the doorway. Neither is there anything behind it for the doorway to lead into. In this way the mysterious emblem gives the appearance of a doorway into nothing. Archeologists call this kind of doorway a *Naos*.

How do we interpret what the C10thBCE sculptor has depicted? What do you imagine we are being shown? If I were to tell you nothing about where this carving was found or how old it was, would that change how you imagine it? What if you didn't know we were in Tel El-Farah and I were to ask you, randomly, out of the blue, *"What do we call a doorway into nothing? A doorway with no building? A doorway that goes nowhere and yet advanced beings from we don't know where can step into our world through that doorway?"* We have a name for that in the twenty-first century. You and I would call it a *portal*.

Surrounding this particular portal, our sculptor has carefully incorporated some other motifs, a crescent moon, and a cluster of stars. What further information is he trying to convey? Now, there is a conventional explanation for these symbols with reference to Hebrew symbology as my guide, Jacob, explains to me.

"There are many kinds of naos," he tells me. *"The one found here at Tel El-Farah, though it shows only a doorway, and it looks like a doorway to nothing, really it represents a whole building, a temple."*

I look at the naos and then back at Jacob, raising a curious eyebrow.

"We consider the building to be implied," he says.

"This figure over the doorway, the crescent, suggests a special time in the month, specifically the new moon. So, this is quite possibly a reference to the new moon Sabbath, which is of course a time of celebration."

"Now, these seven stars over here, when this constellation appears on the horizon it indicates a special time of year, the season of harvest. By bringing these symbols together on the naos, the artist is telling us that here or nearby is a place or a building used for new moon Sabbath celebration and harvest festival."

This all makes very good sense and, having great respect for my scholarly guide Jacob, I suspect it is all true. However, without taking anything away from Jacob's reading, I wonder if there may be another layer of meaning here. Symbolism is a language of many dimensions, and symbols can carry different meanings in different times and places. This was something impressed upon me in my early years of priestly ministry in King's Cross, London. When I was first ordained, the accoutrements of my priestly work in my Roman rite, Anglo-Catholic parish, included rituals dating back centuries and even millennia. In different centuries and in different places, these actions, emblems, and ceremonies carried different meanings.

For example, in each of our three churches, adjacent to the sanctuary, was a small shrine which held what we called *"the reserved sacrament."* This is a piece of consecrated bread, symbolizing the body of Christ. It represented the *"presence"* of Jesus in the building. These shrines mirror the shrine of the *"Show Bread"* within the Jerusalem Temple of Judaism. This was a collection of small loaves of bread placed on a table adjacent to the sanctuary. The loaves were called the *"Bread of the Presence."* So if an ancient Jewish visitor had wandered into our churches, they would observe our ritual, find it strangely familiar and suggest a slightly different interpretation as to what it meant.

In that same parish my grand eucharistic garments included a full-length cassock, a short white tunic, or a white body-length alb, a richly braided dalmatic breastplate, chasuble and stole. In the ritual of Benediction, a full length, richly braided cope would be added to these layers, and if we went outside in procession, a black high-collared cloak would go over the top of everything. By the time of procession, I probably weighed twice what I did before applying these six layers of ecclesiastical robing. At least, I thought they were ecclesiastical layers. Then one day, while idly flicking through the pages of an old, illustrated Bible, I was astonished to see the pen and ink illustration of a person dressed almost exactly like this and carrying a thurible of incense identical to the one we would carry in procession. It was a picture of a Jewish priest serving in the Jerusalem Temple, the one commissioned by King Cyrus of Persia, sometime in the C6thBCE. He even had a beard like mine.

Up until this point I had been perfectly convinced of the Christian symbolic meanings I had been provided with for each ritual and item we used in that parish. The illustration of a priest of another religion from another country in another time confronted me with the reality that many of these things have roots beyond Christianity and that a number of our objects, robes and rituals would also have Jewish significance and Jewish meanings, some similar and some quite different to the Christian explanations I had accepted.

As to our grand processions, these were an essential part of the ceremonial of the Roman empire. A line of officiants with incense-carrying and candle-bearing boys in cassocks and tunics at the front, followed by successive ranks of chasuble-wearing priests at the rear of the procession, provides a very similar display to what you would expect to see at Roman Imperial civic events, in which the order, the vestments, and the accessories all

65

indicated the strata of the imperial hierarchy. A visitor watching our events from an ancient Roman viewpoint would have a pretty shrewd idea as to the messages concerning power and obedience embedded in the dress and ritual of our ecclesiastical events.

Whenever our Bishop would visit for such an event, he would be vested in purple, the colour of the Roman emperor. Purple remained the colour of Roman emperors and their successors even until the close of the Byzantine Empire in 1453CE. Its use as the colour of royalty goes back even earlier than the Roman empire, to the C6thBCE when King Cyrus of Persia chose the colour for himself as a symbol of his ultimate wealth and royal power. On top of all this, the bishop's mitre carries a symbolism for wisdom and teaching reaching back as far as ancient Babylon. This means that my bishop's ecclesiastical attire carried at least five layers of meaning, Christian, Jewish, Roman, Persian and Babylonian.

The reason I am telling you all this is to illustrate the importance of viewing a thing through the lens of more than one culture in order to unwrap all the layers of meaning of an ancient symbol, because there is always more than one layer. With all that in mind, let's return to Tel El-Farah and to these curious symbols on the portal of Asherah and dig a little deeper to find what these signatures may have meant in previous ages. Let's view them through the lens of the Abrahamic source culture. What would a Sumerian observer have to tell us about the naos, the crescent moon, and the cluster of stars? Would an older layer of information emerge? Seen through an ancient Sumerian eye, these carved details go to the very root of Tel El-Farah's harvest festivals. While Tel El-Farah's standing stone marks Asherah's point of arrival, and the portal indicates her means of arrival, the details on the naos mark her point of cosmic origin.

First, let's look again at that crescent moon. In the symbology of ancient Mesopotamia, this symbol represented Nanna, a senior

Powerful One among the Sumerian pantheon, associated with fertility. There's that theme again. A little further back in time in a Sumerian context the crescent moon is really the stylized arc of the horns of a bull and it signifies a region of space, *The Bull* or *Taurus* constellation. Adjacent, the artist has carved a precise cluster of stars which exist in real life within the Bull constellation, sitting on its shoulder. Their number immediately identifies them. These are the stars of the *Pleiades*. We are looking at a star map.

It would be easier to brush this possibility off if it were not for the global scale of this Pleiadean connection. Because all around the world indigenous narratives speak of humanity's great leap forward and relate it to contact with visitors from the stars, and from the stars of the Pleiades in particular. The Cherokee nation on the North American continent, the Aboriginal peoples of Australia and, if my interpretation is correct, the ancient Hebrews of Tel Arad, all carry the same story. From their respective vantage points, different continents and different epochs, each tradition describes primordial tutors in agronomy, who came from a region of deep space, within the Bull constellation, the region known as the Seven Sisters, the stars of the Pleiades.

Three centuries after the carving was made of Asherah appearing in her portal or naos at Tel El-Farah, our narrator at Tel Arad gave us a glimpse of how this memory of visitors from the Pleiades became suppressed and was finally forced out of orthodox Judaism. It is a wonder to me that despite the successive campaigns of Josiah and the Jerusalem redactors over two centuries, I could find the exact same memory of paleocontact in Pernambuco, carried by the descendants of West Africans and indigenous Brazilians. I find it incredible that more than two and a half thousand years later, you and I could attend so similar a harvest festival in Brazil, still honoring the *"Queen of Heaven"* for her tutelage in agriculture and animal husbandry. How is it possible that a full twenty-six centuries after King Josiah's campaign of revisionism, Pope John Paul II would find himself needing to wage the exact same war against indigenous memory of paleocontact and humanity's great leap forward? The parallels are astonishing, and I find the resilience of indigenous memory inspirational. How is it that this information and these rituals have survived? How is that even possible?

The picture I have just shared with you came together for me through a lifetime of world travel and after a long period of seclusion and study, locked down in my shipping crate cabin at the leafy end of my driveway. As I reflect, I am grateful for the timing of these personal discoveries. If I had reached this viewpoint while leading a congregation, it would have been extremely challenging to say the very least. The viewpoint and arguments I am sharing with you in these pages would be quite enough to get a pastor quietly removed from office in many churches. At the very least sermons proposing these views would be sufficient to split most congregations, dividing them into those who have always suspected as much, and others for whom the language of paleocontact or the mention of historic revisions of the Bible is not only taboo, it is simply impossible.

Every week I am contacted by pastors around the world who have reached similar conclusions and who are now wrestling with how to carry that information in a community wedded to seemingly contrary beliefs. Every pastor has to calculate how far they can stretch people in their faith before the elastic of their pastoral relationship reaches breaking point. Every pastor must calculate for a diversity of views and tolerances. For me, it was purely by good fortune, the gift of the universe, that an injury had me laid up in between assignments, thus allowing me the time and energy to follow a white rabbit down the proverbial rabbit hole to see where these questions of redactions and translations would take me. After thirty-three years in church-based ministry, I found the solitude of this season of study in my shipping crate positively re-energizing. At the same time though, as I began to see the full implications of the material I was surveying, there were moments when I had to pause and wonder just how isolating this avenue of research might prove – especially if I chose to publish. On one evening I found myself in a quiet and rather pensive mood, realizing that I was on the cusp of an unstoppable wave. What, I wondered would be the cost for me and my family if I were to move ahead with my plans to publish my first title in paleocontact, *Escaping from Eden.* How many friends would we lose? How much ridicule or push back would we have to face? I put my question to the universe wondering what the answer might be. To my amazement the answer came within a couple of hours. Randomly, from out of the blue, in the middle of a celebrity interview on the TV, the guest (whose name I no longer recall) spoke these words, *"Of course you will lose friends. But you'll gain heaps of others who will value you because of what you are sharing."*

His words leapt out at me as if they had been intended purely for me. This was the answer I needed, and it is exactly what I have found to be true. Through my books, as well as through the community that has built up around *The 5ᵗʰ Kind TV* and the *Paul Wallis* channel, I now find myself surrounded by all kinds of people from all around the world who are ready to listen to a world of ancestral narratives and ask all the questions that back in the day I taught my trainee pastors to ask: *"What kind of narrative is this? Where has this story come from? Is this the original form? And if not, why does it differ? What is this text about as we have it today? What did it mean before?"* And most fundamentally, *"What do the words mean?"* These were the disciplines of source criticism and form criticism which I had carefully taught my trainee pastors over fifteen years. Now as I applied these same questions for myself to a sequence of key words in the Biblical texts, I could see that the data which was emerging was carrying me inescapably into a totally different world. In the chapters that follow I will share more of the data which propelled me into territory that cost me those friends I mentioned before and blew my comfortable world of ministry wide open.

Chapter Five

The Brigadier General and the Sky Council

Jerusalem - 2020

The change wasn't instant. It took a while for the strange world of paleocontact to come into focus for me. Once it did, it still left a very large question hanging. Where does all this re-translation and reframing put Yahweh? If the Bible and its source narratives testify to a whole array of Sky Armies, the *seba hassamayim,* presided over by a Sky Council, the *El Ba'adat* then where does Yahweh figure in that picture?

When referencing this body of non-human overlords the Bible uses the two Hebrew phrases above interchangeably. The name *Seba Hassamayim* hints at the advanced technology of our ancient space invaders. The name *El Ba'adat* reminds us that we are looking at a company of powerful beings. If Yahweh is not the omnipotent, transcendent God we thought he was, does that role fall to somebody else within this advanced company? And if Yahweh is not in charge of project Earth, then who is? To answer this pointy question, we now travel eighty miles north-east of Tel El-Farah to a city at the global epicenter of these ancient dramas. Here we will sit at the feet of a man whose story will sound like something from the canon of *Star Wars* or the *Marvel Universe.* Yet what he has to offer is rooted in more than thirty years of privileged information, gleaned from his senior roles in government and international intelligence.

Thursday 3rd December

For centuries, Jerusalem has been a place of world-changing events and controversy. Today is no different. We are in the company of Raanen Shaked and Gabriel Beharlia, respectively a journalist and photographer for the newspaper, Yediot Aharanot. We are very fortunate to be with them this morning because today they have a scoop. Our guest is Professor Brigadier General Haim Eshed. If you're not familiar with Professor Eshed, his academic and military titles will clue you that he is a very important gentleman in the world of Israeli politics. Professor Eshed is indeed highly respected and very comfortable in his own skin. At eighty-seven years old, he tells us, he has nothing to prove and nothing to lose by coming forward with today's story.

Before his recent retirement, Haim Eshed was Israel's Chief of Space Security. It was a position he held for twenty-eight years. In that time, he headed up Israel's space program, oversighting the Ofek satellite program. So, it is with a considerable weight of credibility that he now puts forward the main thesis of his intriguing new book, *"The Universe Beyond the Horizon."*

With each element of his statement our jaws job a few degrees further. Firstly, Professor Eshed states that the USA and Israel have been in contact with extraterrestrial visitors for decades. Secondly, he suggests that there may be other terrestrial governments also in communication at a covert level. My mind goes to all the US allies around the world and to a tantalizing statement made by Dimitri Medvedev in 2008 when he was Prime-Minister of Russia. Thirdly, Professor Eshed tells us that the terrestrial governments in contact made a compact with a galactic federation of spacefaring civilizations. The compact, apparently, has agreed to a program of research experiments on and around planet Earth, intended to support our visitors in their own intellectual exploration of the fabric of the universe. Fourthly, and most sensationally, Professor Eshed states that we already have access to the necessary technology for interplanetary, and probably interstellar travel, and are collaborating with our

72

neighbours at that level, including in operations on our nearest planetary neighbour, Mars.

The silence in the room is palpable. A true professional, Raanen remains cool and collected as the implications of Professor Eshed's words sink in, but I am sure he is all the while making mental connections between these revelations and other privileged information in his archive. For this reason, Raanen will be aware of the credibility of at least some of what the Brigadier General is saying. At the same time, he is probably also calculating how great a scoop this story may prove to be. For a random stranger to make claims like these is one thing. For these claims to emanate from a man of Professor Eshed's authority is quite another. This really is a scoop.

We turn to the obvious next question. Are our neighbours benevolent or malevolent? Professor Eshed assures us that on more than one occasion our visitors have prevented what could have been nuclear catastrophes. At this point my mind goes to the report by the Russian newspaper Pravda, concerning the presence of a UFO adjacent to reactor four at Chernobyl during the meltdown of 1986. The writer for Pravda speculated that its presence may have been intended to somehow inhibit the meltdown process and prevent the kind of explosion which might have rendered a huge swathe of northern Europe uninhabitable. As my mind whirs, I also recall decades-old reports of nuclear armaments on both the US and Soviet sides of the Cold War being remotely activated and de-activated by an unknown technological intelligence. Could this be what the Brigadier General was referring to? Or might he even be hinting at an ET hand in our international politics of war?

In response to our next question, *"Why has this been kept secret?"* he simply says, *"The visitors have chosen not to self-disclose because the world is not yet ready...They have been waiting until today, for humanity to develop and reach a stage when we will [all] understand what space and spaceships are."*

Apparently though, the world is ready for Haim Eshed's information. A few years ago, he says, he would have been hospitalized for speaking publicly about this. But something has changed. Indeed, Professor Brigadier General Eshed is not the first senior figure to make such statements and remain un-hospitalized. Prime Minister Dimitri Medvedev spoke in very similar terms in 2008 when he told a journalist on a live microphone, that each successive prime minister of Russia is presented with a dossier, detailing the numerous ET civilizations with whom we are already in contact. When the journalist asked him exactly how many such civilizations there were, he answered, *"I wouldn't like to say. It would panic people."* Notably, Prime-Minister Medvedev was not corrected, debunked nor hospitalized for his public disclosure. Similarly, former Minister of Defense for Canada, the late Paul Hellyer, spoke publicly many times about his governments' awareness of present ET contact back when he was in office. He too was not censured or hospitalized.

Dr Edgar Mitchell, the sixth man to walk on the moon, was another public figure who spoke about US government being in contact at a covert level with other spacefaring civilizations. For decades, even though bound by layers of official secrets laws, Dr Mitchell campaigned passionately for official disclosure of this contact, with the hope that we as a spacefaring civilization might take our place at the table alongside our galactic neighbours. I too am passionate about the need for such disclosure. I would like to know who represents us on that council. In whose interests are decisions being made? Is the spectrum of presences on Haim Eshed's Galactic Council the same spectrum as represented in the Bible's accounts of the *El Ba'adat* Sky Council, or the parallel narratives to be found in the Mesopotamian, Norse, Greek or Vedic literature?

In the 1600s Presbyterian Minister Robert Kirk wrote a book called *"The Secret Commonwealth."* It was an exploration of certain ancestral memories carried by the Celtic people of Scotland. Totally at odds with the conservative, puritanical world of seventeenth century Presbyterian Christianity, Kirk argued that, according to Celtic knowledge, no understanding of our world is complete until we realize that above and beyond the visible elites of the world, there is a non-human layer to the governance of project Earth. This is especially the case in the politics of war, and other overarching policies when they present without any sense of value placed on the interests of ordinary human beings. It is, he argued, also evident in our authorities' limited interest in the extraordinary number of people who go missing every year around the globe. All this information is rattling around in my mind as I listen to Haim Eshed refer almost casually to an ET *"program of research experiments on and around planet Earth."* I can't escape the feeling all this information must be connected. Did the Brigadier General keep this statement so brief because, like Prime Minister Dimitri Medvedev, he didn't want to panic people?

What Robert Kirk had to say about the secret layer of human governance matches what the Bible offers us in its glimpses of the operations of the Sky Council in its pages. These vignettes suggest that much of what the ancient elohim did in council was to foment proxy wars with no sense of fellow feeling towards the human beings who were to be the collateral damage incurred by their various spats. For example, in the book of I Kings 22 the prophet Micaiah remote views the Sky Council. By some unexplained, esoteric modality, Micaiah eavesdrops on a conversation in which the Sky Council, hungry for another war, works out how to trick one of the world powers into a foolish and ill-fated attack on another nation. The attack will be based on entirely false intelligence from the king's senior advisors. This is a story with some familiar sounding notes.

The intention of our ancestors is clearly to help us be wise to the operations of this non-human hand, covertly interfering in the peaceful lives of human beings around the world. In the months immediately prior to the decisions which took our planet into the holocaust of the First World War, U.S. President Woodrow Wilson had this to say about some of the most powerful men in US politics and big business at that time: *"They know that there is a power somewhere so organized, so subtle, so watchful, so interlocked, so complete, so pervasive, that they had better not speak above their breath when they speak in condemnation of it."* A generation later, President Eisenhower chose his retirement speech to warn Americans about the dangers of the *"Military Industrial Complex,"* It is possible, he said, *"that public policy could itself become the captive of a scientific-technological elite."*

Our ancestors, including Celtic, Hebrew, Greek and Indian forbears, took their warnings a degree further than these two worthy presidents and asserted that beyond the royals, the political kingmakers, the bankers and technocrats, there exists a non-human layer to the matrix of powers, shaping our world's decision-making. As the Apostle Paul wrote in Ephesians 6, *"For our struggle is not against flesh and blood but…against the rulers of the darkness of the cosmos, against the evil armies of sky spirits."* Again, I have emphasized root meanings in that rendering which reveal the continuity in Paul's thinking with the earlier passages we have explored.

If we return to the insight offered by the Prophet Micaiah in I Kings 22, his eyes on the *"divide and conquer"* politics of the Sky Council forewarns future generations of the possibility of our world leaders being managed and deceived by inscrutable powers or tricked into war by false information. It is also a warning to ordinary people not to be enchanted by a geopolitical message or a *"call to arms"* simply because it has come from the rulers of the day. Micaiah's remote view tells us that this is a danger we need to be forewarned about, lest it should prove to be a pattern that repeats. That is the profound and important take home meaning of the Prophet Micaiah's account in the book of I Kings.

However, the moment the Sky Council is interpreted as something divine, and its president translated as *"God"*, this vital geopolitical insight is lost, because the actions of God must be holy and therefore cannot be questioned. There is a very shrewd understanding of the workings of the world on offer once we strip away the false translations which have made these narratives out to be God-stories. In this way the conventional word-choices favoured by mainstream Bible translations have robbed us of what was previously on offer, namely a clear lens on geopolitical events and the world around us. Without the insight of Micaiah's remote view of the powerful being on the Sky Council whose job was to deceive, we are left to simply trust and believe what the powers tell us.

At this point it might be interesting to ask who occupies the chair of this curious council. Whether Haim Eshed's Galactic Federation or the prophet Micaiah's Sky Council, we might want to know who exactly is running the show. In the Hebrew scriptures the presiding figure is identified by a mysterious name, *El Elyon.* In Zambia, speakers of the Bemba language recognize that word. In Bemba, *elyoni* identifies the feathered entities who observe us from on high. It is the Bemba word for *bird.* So my Zambian friends will not be surprised that when we go to the root meaning of the Hebrew word *elyon* we find the concept of being above. Though conventionally translated as *"the highest"* or *"the Most High,"* *elyon* is more strictly a relative term which means *"above the others"* or *"higher than the rest."* The implication of this language is a position of command. Dr. Jeff A. Benner of the Ancient Hebrew Research Center argues that the root of the word *elyon* comes from two pictograms, representing an eye, and a shepherd's staff, perfectly combining the two ideas of oversight and control. In that sense we can see *el elyon* as a title or functional label. It tells us nothing about who or what is in the chair, simply that one of the powerful ones is higher than or senior to the others.

Professor Emanuel Tov of the Hebrew University of Jerusalem is one of the most highly respected Jewish exegetes. In his critical analysis of the Biblical Hebrew text, Professor Tov writes that the names or titles *Elyon, El* and *Yahweh* correspond to three different individuals. Among the many elohim in the Hebrew scriptures, my friend Mauro Biglino claims to have identified twenty distinct and separate beings, a few of whom we detailed in the previous chapter. But while there are many elohim there is only one Elyon. The pictographic representation of Elyon as the one with oversight and control perfectly corresponds with the role of Elyon as it plays out in relation to the other elohim of the Biblical narratives.

It's worth noting the narrator's invocation of the language of height when discussing ancient powerful beings. Why higher? Does it mean taller? Does it mean more elevated in altitude? Or does it just mean senior? This association of superior powers with a position *"higher in space"* repeats in ancestral narrative all around the world. For instance, if we listen to the stories of beginnings told by the Edo people of Nigeria and southern Benin, we will hear of Osanabua, the almighty one *above* the waters. The Efik people of Nigeria also have stories of beginning which carry a memory of advanced non-human beings terraforming our environment and genetically modifying our ancestors. They are called Abassi and Atai. They too look down from the sky to survey their human creations. Once again, their superiority and seniority is demonstrated by their situation, high above everyone else, residing in their island in the sky. It is possible that early encounters between human beings and advanced visitors, conflated in our minds the ideas of being high and being advanced, thereby equating the concepts of being higher with being senior.

The Bible's source narratives in the annals of ancient Sumeria, again would reinforce this idea of an order of command among our visitors. Enlil is the commander of this region of space. He has seniority over Enki who is stationed down here in command of project Earth. So, this notion that the advanced beings are commanders in an ascending and descending chain of command is present in the source narrative.

Deuteronomy 32:8 shows Elyon in his position of command over the Sky Council, parceling the humans out among the elohim. If we read this moment in the Septuagint, the Greek translation of the Hebrew scriptures, it says the nations were distributed among the *"angelwn theou"* which means among the *"agents of God."* However, we know that here the Greek *theou* is a rendering of the Hebrew Elyon. So, the text is telling us the peoples are being apportioned to the agents of Elyon. The Qumran texts says that the peoples are distributed to the *"benei elohim."* We could say *"to the class of elohim,"* to *"those of elohim-kind."*

Verses 8 and 9 show Yahweh's moment in this distribution. It says: *"For Yahweh's portion, the people of Jacob, [for] the place of his inheritance, he found him in a desert land, a wastelend."*

This snapshot really frames the story of the people of Yahweh and their trials in the desert. He and they are going to have a hard time.

Deuteronomy 32:8 is one of many moments in the Bible in which the world of the ancients is portrayed as being divided into a patchwork of human colonies each with their own allotted Powerful One to govern over them and put them to work. This is the coherent picture of the human condition which plays out all through the Hebrew Canon. But what is most interesting about this picture is where it positions the character Yahweh. It is possible that you are not familiar with this name. You may be more familiar with another way of writing that name, *Jehovah*. The name is absent from many Christian Bibles, having been translated into something else. In many Christian Bibles where you see the title *The LORD*, all in capitals, this is the translators' idiom for rendering the name Yahweh. This translation is a theological interpretation, equating Yahweh with God. However, as we have just seen, Yahweh is in fact the junior of El Elyon, one of a number of subordinate elohim, each receiving their particular share of the planet's spoils from the more senior entity.

This is only one of many texts which reveal that we cannot equate Yahweh with the idea of a transcendent, cosmic God. So, who is he then? What is Yahweh if he is not the senior figure in this ancient pantheon? Moreover, what are the Biblical stories of Yahweh if at root they are not stories about God? The great question of what Yahweh really represents is precisely what we will explore in the next few pages. But get ready. If what I have shared to this point has rattled the cages of long held beliefs and assumptions about life, the universe and everything, the next chapter is going to take us deeper still into a world of even more sensitive taboos. This is territory where only the boldest dare to go. Are you ready?

Chapter Six

What Kind of Father?

"Paul, thanks for the coffee, but this is where I know you really have lost the plot! Let's get back to basics here. Christianity is the religion of Jesus. His name in the original Hebrew is Yeshua. It means 'From Yahweh, Salvation.' Your view of Yahweh as anything other than God is a total contradiction of two thousand years of Christian faith."

Lance is a ministry-friend who has always felt a liberty to be free and frank in his theological pronouncements. We trained at theological college together and served alongside each other in the Anglican Diocese of London back in the day. He has always prided himself in being orthodox to the bone, and what he has just said would represent the view of many orthodox Christian believers around the world. Many would pipe up and say, *"Yahweh is God and Jesus is God's son,"* as if this were an article of faith. Except it isn't.

The name Yahweh is, in fact, nowhere mentioned in the universal Creeds of the Church. The language of the Creeds is *"God,"* *"Father,"* and *"Almighty."* Not *"Yahweh."* In an intriguing encyclical sent around the episcopal conferences and parishes of the Catholic world in 2008, Pope Benedict XVI urged that the name Yahweh should not be used in the prayers and liturgies of the churches because, *"It is not a Christian name for God."*

That's interesting. Why isn't it? If it is a Jewish name for God, then why did the Pope want to assert it is not a Christian name for God? I should clarify. I am not a Roman Catholic priest. My ordination is in the Anglican Church *(The Church of England or The Episcopalian Church, as its branch is known in the U.S.)* Over thirty-three years my ministry extended into Pentecostal, charismatic, and non-aligned streams. So, usually, I don't pay a great deal of attention to the edicts of Roman Catholic cardinals and prelates, and I don't tend to read the encyclicals and bulls of our successive popes. On this point, however, Benedict XVI and I are in perfect agreement.

"Lance, I totally follow your logic, except there is no preposition in the name of Jesus, as you suggest. You say Yeshua means "From Yahweh, Salvation," but I might just as easily say his name means "Salvation from Yahweh!" In fact, I think that Jesus saving us from Yahweh would be truer to Jesus' underlying attitude towards Yahweh in the Gospels."

Slowly and methodically over coffee at the Tipsy Bull in downtown Canberra, I show Lance the clues in the Gospels that Jesus, whatever the correct spin of his name, was in reality not a Yahwist. To be fair I have to take my hat off to Lance for patiently sitting through my informal presentation, because I know I am striking at what, for him, is a fundamental presupposition of faith. I know it must sting for him to hear what I am saying. But the implications of getting this wrong are just too great to politely tiptoe around the question. If we can talk it over calmly, then let's do so. So I start out by showing my friend from text to text how Jesus repeatedly repudiates the laws of Yahweh, otherwise known as the *Laws of Moses*, or simply *The Law*.

Throughout the Gospel of Matthew Jesus is heard saying, *"Moses said this. But I say this!"* The idea that Jesus could cancel and replace a law understood to be the divine word of God would have been impossible for his devout Jewish hearers. To the minds of his hearers, Jesus was defaming the very idea of the law's divine authorship. Indeed, Jesus was clear. Something better than the

Yahwistic law was now on offer. In one place in the Gospel of Matthew, Jesus states that his hearers would need to think in terms of ethics higher than those of *"the Scribes and the Pharisees,"* who studied and taught studying them as the recognized authorities in Yahweh's laws. Jesus' statement about exceeding their righteousness is often taken to be a criticism only of the integrity of the Scribes and the Pharisees themselves. However, the laws they followed, and followed assiduously were the laws of Yahweh. So it isn't hard to see that Jesus is suggesting there is a better moral code than the laws of Yahweh. How were his hearers to understand this statement? If Jesus believed the laws of Yahweh were not good enough and needed to be discarded and replaced with something better, then he was surely asserting that the laws of Yahweh were neither eternal nor divine. What did that say about his view of Yahweh?

While that theological time-bomb slowly ticked away, the first generation of Christian believers wrestled with the question of whether Jesus really had written off the laws of Yahweh. This fraught debate, which divided even Jesus' apostles, was stoked by the seeming ambiguity of another of Jesus' most famous utterances, recorded in the Gospel of Matthew.

"Until heaven and earth pass away not a jot or a tittle shall disappear from the law... until everything is accomplished." (Matthew 5:17)

What did Jesus mean by that? Some took this saying as an assertion that the Laws of Yahweh were eternal, remaining in force forever *"until heaven and earth pass away."* However, this reading does not square at all with the delete and replace approach, evident in Jesus' teachings in other places. And, glaringly, there is another timeframe indicated in the very same saying: *"Until everything is accomplished."* *Until* means there is an end date on it. *Accomplished* is a completed action, like completed, fulfilled, done and dusted. These words would indicate that the Yahwistic law has an end date on it, and that a time will come when it will no longer be in force. To put it more colloquially Jesus is saying, *"The Law of Yahweh will never change, not by the tiniest degree UNTIL everything is accomplished. Then it will be over, done and dusted, sayonara!"*

To be fair, though, it is easy to see how the two timeframes of Jesus' saying would throw up a heap of confusion. However, this confusion led ultimately to the convening of a remarkable council in Jerusalem around 50CE, which drew together the key leaders of the primitive church. Their agenda was to settle the matter once and for all. For years there had been a growing gulf among the early believers regarding the two different perspectives on the status of Yahweh and his laws in the new religion of Christianity. Some, like James and Peter, were advancing the view that Jesus had instituted a set of religious beliefs, built on a reformed Josiah-style Judaism. They read the current Yahwist redaction of the Hebrew canon and took it at face value. They saw Christianity as being built on faith in and obedience to Yahweh. By contrast, other central apostolic figures, notably the Apostle Paul and Joseph of Cyprus (a.k.a. Barnabas) argued that Jesus had put a decisive end to the regime of Yahweh's laws. His laws were neither the foundation nor even requisite in the new way of Christianity.

Although this appeared to be an insoluble conflict between two diametrically opposed views of Yahweh, the Jerusalem Council resolved the disagreement decisively. In part the day was carried on the basis of experiential arguments. This is because it was clear to everyone present that powerful spiritual phenomena were being experienced by the Yahwists and the anti-Yahwists alike. The cosmos didn't seem to discriminate. All had to agree that the Spirit was to be found among all kinds of people, whether they be

Yahwists, anti-Yahwists or people who had never even heard of Yahweh. The council finally ruled that the era of faith in and obedience to the laws of Yahweh was over.

Yet a matter of scriptural interpretation could not be settled on the basis of experience alone. The council's decision to set aside faith in and obedience to The Torah, would have been completely impossible if the entire council had not finally become convinced that Jesus had put clear blue water between his way and the stories and laws of Yahweh. If Jesus had reaffirmed Yahweh and Yahwism, that fact on its own would have been sufficient to settle the whole debate. What the council saw was that on careful analysis Jesus had cumulatively put so much distance between himself and the Yahweh narrative that it proved insupportable to require followers of Jesus to also be Yahwists. What was it in the teachings of Jesus that finally convinced all concerned, James, Peter, Paul, Barnabas, and the full spectrum of apostolic leaders, that to reaffirm the laws of Yahweh would be impossible and wrong? I would identify four key moments in the teachings of Jesus which would have sealed the deal:

Firstly, Jesus never used the name Yahweh as a name for God. It's that simple. End of story. Just let that gold nugget of information sink in for a moment.

Secondly, Jesus presented his own experience of God, the Source of the Cosmos, as something unknown to his devout Jewish apostles. As devout Jews of the first century, Jesus' closest followers knew Yahweh and knew him well. They had been schooled in the ways of Yahweh since infancy. But they did not know the Cosmic God the *"pater en tois ouranois"* the *"father in the heavens"* of Jesus. In John 14, Jesus speaks these words to the people sitting in front of him, who were all devout Jewish believers: *"If you really knew me, you would know my Father as well."* Apparently, whoever these devout Jews knew as God it was not the one Jesus called *"Father."*

Jesus' apostle, Philip then asks Jesus, *"Show us The Father!"* This is Philip's acknowledgement that he and the other disciples are not familiar with the God whom Jesus addresses as *"Father."* It is noteworthy that Jesus does not respond to Philip by saying, *"Of course you already know the Father. Haven't you read the teachings of Moses and the stories of Yahweh?"* On the contrary, he points to himself and says, *"Anyone who has seen me has seen The Father."* In this intimate conversation, which is all about seeing Jesus as an emanation of the *"Father,"* the name *Yahweh* is nowhere to be seen.

Thirdly, Jesus starkly asserted that the *"father"* served by the devout teachers of the Torah was not God. In John 8 Jesus addresses a crowd of die-hard Yahwists and tells them this: *"You are of the father, of the devil. And it is your father's desires you wish to follow. He was a murderer and a liar from the beginning, and never represented the truth, because there is no truth in him. When he speaks a lie, he is speaking his mother tongue, because he is a liar and the father of lies. But because I speak the truth you do not believe me."*

Here Jesus asserts that there is a night and day difference between his own ethics and truth-telling and the shocking immorality of the *"father"* so revered by this audience of Yahweh-worshippers.

Jesus declares that his own Source is something prior to Moses, which means prior to Yahweh. His source is prior even to the patriarch, Abraham. Jesus says, *"Before Abraham was I am."*

It is something truly painful to read generations of religious commentaries as they contort themselves in an effort to dance around the obvious message of these words. The God and Father of the Jewish leaders and their people, known to them by the name Yahweh, was not an entity whom Jesus in any way wished to affirm as God. His language of *murderer, liar, father of lies* and *devil* could hardly be more emphatic. Yet somehow, Jesus had a way of saying things that could rile people up in the moment, yet still leave them puzzling hours and days after his departure, scratching their heads and asking one another, *"What did he just say?"*

Fourthly, Jesus, Jesus loved to speak of the Source of the Cosmos as *"Father,"* and in his teachings he directed his followers to speak directly to their *pater en tois ouranois,* their *father in the heavens.* In total contrast he mercilessly mocked the idea that the entity Yahweh could be regarded as any kind of father. This percussive moment is reported in Matthew 7 and Luke 11. While teaching about prayer, Jesus says, *"If you evil lot know how to give good gifts to your own children when they ask you, how much more will your Cosmic Father (Heavenly Father) give good gifts to those who ask him?!"* Jesus then goes on to contrast the benevolent attitude of the Cosmic Father with the opposite behaviour of Yahweh. He says, *"Which of you fathers if his children asked for food and drink would give them a stone? Which of you fathers would respond to the cries of his hungry and thirsty children by giving them a snake?"* Exactly! Implicitly he is asking, *"What kind of father would do something so cruel and perverse?"* Jesus asks, knowing there is an answer, and knowing that his audience knows the answer.

This saying might wash over many modern readers as nothing more than a perverse and ridiculous scenario, randomly picked by Jesus as a dramatic way of making his point. Yet it is so much more than that. In these words, Jesus is appealing to a well-known story about Yahweh from the Torah. It is a direct reference to the experience of the Children of Israel, hungry and thirsty in the wilderness, crying out to Yahweh for help, depleted by homelessness, hunger and thirst and fed up with their emergency daily ration of manna – a word which means *"we don't even know what it is."* Yahweh's response to his people's cries for water was to point them to a stone with instructions as to how to get water from the stone. This happens twice. When the people dare to complain, Yahweh responds by releasing snakes among his people to bite them as a punishment for their insolence in moaning about being hungry and thirsty. As a consequence of the snakes, many of the people become gravely ill and great numbers of them die. Jesus' original hearers would have recognised the reference immediately. What kind of *"father"* is Yahweh to treat desperate people like that? It is unconscionable. Yahweh is clearly no kind of father. And Jesus insists that GOD the Cosmic Source is nothing like that. This saying is a body blow to the view that equates Yahweh with the God and Father of Jesus.

The decision of the Jerusalem Council of 50CE made clear that the Yahwistic laws should not be regarded as divinely eternal, and neither was belief in or obedience to the Torah to be required. The stipulation which issued from their discussion was that all believers should avoid meat with the blood still in it, they should conduct themselves well in terms of sexual behaviour and avoid being a part of the worship of anything less than God, by which they meant, *"The source of the cosmos and everything in it, that I which we all live and move and have our being, of whom we are all offspring."* (Apostle Paul, Acts 17.)

In the early decades and centuries of the Christian church, significant leaders, known as *"Church Fathers,"* put meat on the bones of this new religion of Jesus. In the C3rdCE, Origen unpacked further the implications of the Jerusalem Council's decision two centuries before. He argued powerfully that the elohim and Yahweh stories should not be read as if they were portrayals of the God and Father of Jesus. Indeed, he said that if we took the elohim and Yahweh narratives at face value we would have to believe of God, *"such things as we would not believe of the most savage and unjust of men."*

The reason Origen felt compelled to highlight this matter is that the Church had somehow overlooked the ruling of the Jerusalem Council and glued the Yahwistic redaction of the Hebrew Scriptures onto the writings of Jesus' apostles and others to create a Christian Bible, comprising the Old Testament and the New. The very act of enclosing this spectrum of stories within the binding of a single cover sent the unfortunate message that the *"God"* of the Hebrew Scriptures, known as Yahweh, was the same God and Father whom Jesus affirmed and taught about. Origen did his level best to prevent this equation from establishing itself in the minds of believers. However, ultimately, he did not succeed, and a later generation of church fathers had Origen censured and recast as a heretic.

The Church's decision to identify God with the violence and inhumanity of many of the elohim has created an unfolding catastrophe through all the ages since. All manner of abuses, misogyny, colonizations and enslavements have been justified in the name of a *"God"* who looks, sounds and acts like the elohim of the ancient stories. What this equation has done to our psychology as a species, and our geopolitics as a civilization is something I explore in greater depth in my book *The Scars of Eden.* However, there is only so much theology that can be unravelled over the course of two cappuccinos. For now, I just want to show my friend Lance that the idea of Jesus saving people from Yahweh might not be as far-fetched as he might think. In fact the idea becomes unavoidable once we confront the reality of the Yahweh stories and ask, *"What do these texts reveal about the moral character of this mysterious entity?"*

To reframe our understanding of who or what Yahweh might have been, we should return to the moment when he first appears in the stories of the Bible. This puts us in Midian, standing in front of something which has the Egyptian exile, Moses, baffled. Some kind of entity is speaking with Moses out of what he describes as a bush which carried a fire, without the bush burning up. Precisely what the bush and fire might have been is something to wonder at. The greater issue though is who or what this other interlocutor might be because it's clear that Moses has no idea who he is talking to.

Imagine receiving a call on your cell phone and reading *"Caller ID Unknown"* on the screen. If you choose to pick up and hear an unfamiliar voice speaking to you, you will have to stop them at some point, and ask, *"Sorry, who am I speaking to?"* This is the situation Moses now finds himself in. The bush is not the person speaking and neither is the fire. Whatever they really are they are only the medium or device through which Moses can hear the voice of this mysterious unknown entity. The speaker introduces himself as *"the Powerful One of [Moses'] ancestors."* If this were true, isn't it rather odd that Moses doesn't recognise him? Perhaps the problem is that Moses is unable to see the other speaker. He can hear a voice and see a fire, but he can't see the entity itself. What we can say is that this mysterious entity, who claims to be the Powerful One known by his ancestors, for some reason introduces himself with a name that Moses has never heard before, *Yahweh.*

By the end of the C6thBCE when the final redaction of the Hebrew Scriptures had been completed, the word Yahweh had come to be used as a name or title for God – the Source of the Cosmos. What is very clear however is that it did not mean that in the beginning. Moses has no idea what the word Yahweh means. Evidently it is not a Hebrew or Aramaic word. Neither is it an

Egyptian word. It doesn't appear to belong to any language Moses is aware of. Twenty-first century linguists will tell you that it is a word with no etymology or history in the Hebrew language. Essentially, we are looking at a foreign word, a word from another unknown language. It is what linguists call a loan word.

To illustrate for you what a loan word is let me take you to Sicily and the south of Italy in the late 1950's. Here linguists found themselves baffled by a funny word which had been appearing in the language of the street, a word that they had never heard before, a word that means *spade*. However the Italian language already had a perfectly regular word for spade – *la pala*. So what was this other word? It sounded like *sciavelo*, yet as they spelled it out it appeared to be a word with no etymology or history in the Italian language. Poring over its component parts, the linguists couldn't find any root with a meaning of a digging item, nor any indication of a meaning or origin.

It took linguists a while to realise that this mystifying word had appeared at a time in history when there was a significant movement of people, originally from Sicily and the south of Italy, returning home from time spent in America post the Second World War. When they returned, they brought with them an American word, *shovel*. Now back in the mother country, they used the Italian sound system to pronounce the American word, and Italian spelling conventions to transcribe it. That is how a loan word works. It appears in the sound system of the host language with no local ancestry or etymology.

That is exactly how the word Yahweh makes its appearance in the Hebrew Canon. We therefore have to think of *YHWH*, originally written with no vowels, as a foreign sound, with no meaning attached to it, and go from there. In a few pages I will reveal that considering *YHWH* as the memory of a sound, rather than a memory of meaning, opens up a possibility which makes sense of the moral problems that exist around the behaviour of the Yahweh character. At the same time this avenue of exploration will fundamentally challenge our whole idea of what the Bible is all about.

Back to Midian. When Moses asks, *"Sorry who am I talking to?"* he doesn't really get an answer. Yahweh tells him *"I am as I am."* It is kind of a non-answer, as if Yahweh is saying, *"That's for me to know and for you to find out."* However, within a sentence or so the entity has begun to refer to himself using the name Yahweh. He begins his dialogue with Moses saying, *"Tell them 'I am has sent you.' Say, 'The I am of Israel has sent me.'"* Then within a sentence he says, *"Tell the people that Yahweh the Powerful One of their ancestors has sent you to them."*

Do the enigmatic words *"I am"* give us a further insight as to the identity of this mysterious Yahweh? They do if we look at how this moment is handled in the pages of the Septuagint. This was the Greek translation of the Hebrew Canon used by Jesus and those who wrote for him. The Septuagint's version of this conversation has Yahweh saying, *"Tell them I am The Being! Say this to the children of Israel, 'The Being has sent me to you!'"*

Not a lot of extra information then! It only returns us to the question of what kind of *"being"* Yahweh might be. For an insight, we could ask who Yahweh thinks he is. In fact, there are a number of Biblical texts which answer this exact question so that we can say unequivocally that Yahweh sees himself as one of the Powerful Ones. In that very first conversation with Moses, Yahweh says *"I am the Powerful One of your ancestors."* In the Ten Commandments he says that his people must serve *"no other powerful one."* In a moment where he is angered by his king seeking a medical prognosis from the powerful one of neighbouring Ekron, Yahweh says, *"Is there no Powerful one here..."* indicating himself, *"whom he could consult?"* In this way

Yahweh identifies both himself and the ruler of Ekron as both being elohim or powerful ones.

As we saw in chapter three, there are many kinds of powerful one occupying places on the Sky Council of the Biblical narratives. What kind is Yahweh? Is he a spirit who can translocate in the blink of an eye? Is he huge and terrifying like Behemoth in the book of Job? Is he a humanoid like the entities with whom Abraham and Sarah interact in Genesis 18? A clue can be found in the letters of the tetragrammaton, *YHWH*, if we do as I suggested before and consider *YHWH* as a sequence of sounds.

If you have read my book *Echoes of Eden*, you will already know where I am going with this. But, if you will permit me, in the next couple of pages I need to lay out the key information afresh to show the logic for the most fundamental and far-reaching paradigm-shift in my research journey to-date. It is a shift which reframes how we look on human history, and overturns nearly two thousand years of dogma as to what the Bible is all about. If, on the other hand, you are new to the idea that *YHWH* may be the memory of a sound, rather than a memory of meaning, then what I am about to say may take a while to process. When we get to the punchline, I hope you will be willing to suspend your initial disbelief and follow my logic through to the next chapter. Having done that, it will probably be a good moment to put the kettle on, pour yourself a cup of tea, or maybe a glass of something stronger, and just sit for a while to digest what I am about to tell you.

Because prior to Qumran Hebrew and later Masoretic Hebrew, the script for the Hebrew language did not include vowels, we don't know how *YHWH* was originally pronounced. In the original transliteration of the sounds we have only the four consonants. Yet I would argue that those four consonants are sufficient to place the Yahweh narratives within a global family of stories, which cast a very different light on what the Yahweh narratives may have been before they became stories about GOD.

The clue is in that pair of *H*s. When we insert vowels into the YHWH the *H*s almost disappear. They become almost silent. In the beginning however they were not. As languages evolve through centuries, sounds modify. A familiar pattern of change is the process of affrication. Essentially it is a pattern of sound-softening. Over time hard plosive sounds soften to become fricatives:

t becomes *ts* becomes *s*

d becomes *dz* becomes *z*

b becomes *bv* becomes *v* *becomes w*

k becomes *ch* (as in the Scottish lo*ch* or the German a*ch*t) becomes a *h*

It is that last progression that relates to *YHWH*. In Proto-North-west Semitic, the linguistic ancestor of modern Hebrew, the *h-h* sound was vocalised quite differently. Instead of the almost silent glottal fricative it is today, it was a harder velar fricative - a *ch-ch* sound. Further back the *ch-ch* sound may well have been the harder plosive *k-k*. The significance of this story of affrication is that all around the world, ancient indigenous cultures tell stories of a time when human beings were governed over by powerful beings who were not human. Indeed, they were described in very non-human terms. They had hard armour-like skin, they had tails and some of them had feathers. Some exhaled breath which could be ignited and used as a weapon. To all intents and purposes, they are what today we would call a dragon. The red flag for us is that many of these mysterious beings carry the *k-k* or *ch-ch* in their names.

Kukulkan, Ququmatz, Quetzalcoatl governed the Mayan, Toltec and Aztec peoples of ancient Mesoamerica.

Coca ruled over human society in Portugal and Spain

Ikyuchu, Kyucedra ruled over Japan.

Kholkhis ruled over Georgia.

The Draig *Coch* ruled over the people of Wales

Akhekh was the Powerful One of Egypt.

Could these names, from diverse language-groups all around the world, be carrying the memory of the same sound? Do these names represent an ancestral memory of how these mysterious beings sounded to the humans who first encountered them in the deep past? Could this *ch-ch* be an echo of the abrasive sound of their breath as they approached? Think of all the horror films you have watched in which it is the *ch-ch* of raspy breath that first clues you that the monster is lurking in the shadows!

If you're not yet persuaded by this unlikely array of correlations, the last name, the Egyptian one, is the one to really note. This is because of a very revealing moment in the book of Joshua. In the twenty-fourth chapter, we hear Joshua, the leader of the people of Israel, the successor of Moses, delivering a speech at Shechem in modern day Jordan. Schechem was a place of great significance for the tribes of Israel. It is a place where Abraham and Israel (otherwise known as Jacob) both built grand temples. It is here that Joshua gathers the people gather to hear his landmark speech. Drawing on all his rhetorical power, Joshua calls upon the gathered crowd to choose today whom they will serve. Knowing the names of Egypt's powerful one, as we do, we understand that Joshua is asking the people to choose whether they will serve *ACH ECH* of Egypt or *yACHwECH* of Israel.

Did you see that? The similarity of the two names is striking. They are almost the same. Once you have seen it, you cannot unsee it. This similarity makes it even more obvious that Joshua is presenting Egypt's powerful one *ACH ECH* and Israel's powerful one *yACHwECH* as direct and precise counterparts. Both are to be served in the same kind of way and both, I would argue, are the same kind of entity. And just in case you didn't remember, *Akhekh* of Egypt (as he is spelt today) was a dragon.

Time for that cup of tea?

Chapter Seven

The Silent Coup and the Great Redaction

England – when I was a boy

I may be no more than six, but I am not going to be fobbed off with nonsense like this. I am debriefing with my dad after a school assembly which has got me annoyed. I love my school in leafy Buckinghamshire, England, but it isn't hard for me to see how my school has taken Christianity and used it as a tool for crowd control. School Christianity is a religion full of *oughts* and *thou shallt nots*. The Gospel of school Christianity can probably best be summarised in the line from the famous Christmas carol which says, *"Christian children all must be mild, obedient, good as he."* To my young mind the whole God-story presented by my school has the look and feel of a total fabrication, designed purely to get the kids to behave.

"I mean, dad, my teachers say all these things about God, but they've never met him! They have never seen him! For all they know God could be a great, giant, green dragon!"

From behind the page of his daily paper, my dad simply says, *"Yes, you're probably right."*

Half a century later I discover that both his and my words may have been a good deal closer to the truth than either he or I had realised. Only in my mature life has my research returned me to my childhood question, not by suggesting that God was a giant dragon, rather it was the Yahweh character, now confused with God, who fitted the bill. This is not an easy paradigm-shift to achieve. I wouldn't even attempt to put this thought to Pastor Lance over any number of cappuccinos. This is because in

Christianity the image of the Dragon or the Serpent (the Bible uses the two words interchangeably) is interpreted as an image of evil. The idea of associating dragon imagery with Yahweh is anathema. And yet, once again, I have not stuck my neck out as far as you might think. Because it is the Bible itself which associates Yahweh with dragon imagery.

The New Testament book of Revelation 13 describes an entity simply known as The Beast. The writer says: *"The beast I saw was like a leopard. Its feet were as the feet of a bear and its jaws like the jaws of a lion."* If that picture were not disturbing enough, look and see where the writer of revelation has got this description from. It comes from the Hebrew scriptures, in the book of Hosea. In its pages we read of YHWH's rage over the people of Israel who have dispensed with his services and seem to have forgotten about him. In his fury, YHWH determines to send the people of Israel a little reminder of who he is:

"I will be to them like a lion. I will lurk by the road like a leopard. I will meet them as a bear, deprived of its cubs, and will rip open their rib cage and eat them alive. I will devour them like a lion. Like a wild beast I shall tear their bodies apart." This threat of bloody violence and murder begins with the words, *"I am Yahweh, your Powerful One, ever since the land of Egypt."* He concludes his violent threat with a flourish, saying, *"You are destroyed, Israel! I am your only help. I will be your king, there is no one out there to save you."* This is YHWH describing himself. Nice! In some Bibles, above the flourish of these last two sentences, editors have written the unlikely subheading, *"Yahweh's Mercy."* Oh my! If that is YHWH's mercy, then heaven help us!

Let me just summarise the psychology of YHWH's message (according to Hosea.) *"I will murder you horribly because you have displeased me. Nobody will be able protect you from me. I will get to you! But if you please me I will forgive you and protect you. Because nobody else loves you like I do or even cares for you. I am all you've got."* Let's call a spade a spade. This is the language of a psychopath.

Psychopathic doublethink of this kind is powerfully dramatized in the episode in Numbers 21, referenced by Jesus, in which YHWH sends *seraphim* to bite the people. It is seraphim (the same word) who the Jewish prophet Isaiah witnesses acting as deputies for YHWH and empowering him to act as a go-between. This is in a text traditionally read at the coronation of Christian kings and queens. Interesting choice.

The root of the word *seraphim* means *"fiery ones"* or *"the ones that burn."* The use of the words in the book of Isaiah, indicates that a *sarap* or *seraph* (the singular of *seraphim)* is a flying serpent known for its fire. Just picture that for a moment. Can anyone say *dragon*? I am in good company in terms of joining these dots because the writer of Revelation in the New Testament uses the word dragon (*drakwn - Greek*) and seraphim (*ophin - Greek*) interchangeably. (Revelation 12 and 20)

The word *hannahas* also makes an appearance in the Numbers 21 report of the biting incident, and it is the regular word for a plain and simple snake. Here is one example of its use from the book of Amos from the C8thBCE:

"YHWH says, 'Disaster for you who long for the Day of Yahweh. What will the Day of Yahweh mean for you? It will mean darkness, not light, like when someone escapes from a lion only to be confronted with a bear; or when a man goes into his house and puts his hand on the wall only for a snake (hannahas) to bite him.'" (Amos 5)

However, when YHWH sends seraphim to attack his people, Numbers 21 uses both words – *sarap/seraphim* and *hannahas* - to make clear that this nasty episode involved something more than bites from plain and simple snakes. To be bitten by a snake is bad enough. A bite from a flying, fiery serpent suggests something of a different order. This was the punishment which YHWH inflicted upon his people for the sin of complaining about their emergency rations. And as the story goes, many people died as a result. But there is a post-script to the story – and herein lies another example of YHWH's *"mercy."* YHWH informs his wounded and dying people that their one chance of rescue is to bow down and worship. But worship what?

We would surely expect YHWH to require his people to bow down and worship him. In the event YHWH has a bronze dragon crafted and insists that anyone who refuses to kowtow to the image of the bronze dragon will die. The logic of this moment is surely that YHWH is forcing the people to re-establish their obedience and worship of him. However, in the Ten Commandments YHWH strictly forbade the representation of any Powerful One other than himself. His people are not allowed to depict other Powerful Ones or ever bow down to them. The only way YHWH's command to worship the Bronze Dragon can be squared with the first of YHWH's Ten Commandments is if the Bronze Dragon is a representation of himself.

If the Bronze Dragon is not a representation of YHWH then there is no logic to his command for the people to kowtow to it. It would make no sense at all for YHWH to predicate people's healing on their worshiping someone or something other than himself. However, if the Bronze Dragon is a representation of YHWH, then his insistence that the people worship it fits perfectly into the dynamic of that moment. It is the same psychopathic mentality which says, *"I smite you. And I save you, but only if you worship me."* So to repeat the question originally framed by Jesus' teaching on prayer, what kind of *"Father"* treats human beings begging him for help like that?

In time, the Bronze Dragon came to be known as *Nehushtan* and it became a sacred object in the collection of YHWH's special things for the tabernacle and the Jerusalem Temple. Neither did the people forget the episode, both the trauma of it but also the promise of healing to those who would gaze on the Nehushtan and venerate it. This cultural memory was so resilient that six centuries later, II Kings 18 reports that Jewish believers were still worshiping the Bronze Nehushtan, secreted in the temple of Solomon, in the late C7thBCE. This was a period when King Hezekiah's reforms were foreshadowing the great reforms under King Josiah. The writer of II Kings lists the major physical items which Hezekiah's royal guard set about destroying. These objects included many wooden carvings of Asherah, and many of the high places and standing stones, associated with ancient stories of paleocontact. The Nehushtan, was also destroyed in this great purge. It too represented an era of face-to-face contact with the Powerful Ones of Israel's past.

Yet the destruction of the Nehushtan, the Bronze Dragon, would seem strange. The book of II Kings in its current form, exists to teach Yahwistic monotheism. So the existence of the Nehushtan and the continuing tradition of bowing in worship towards it, and the kind of being it appeared to represent, were all a matter of considerable inconvenience to the YHWHist agenda of II Kings. So the fact that the book's narrator feels he has to acknowledge the Nehushtan at all adds credibility to the information surrounding it. But did Hezekiah's soldiers know what it was when they destroyed it? Did they not know that this was a sacred object, crafted on YHWH's personal instruction? Did they not see it as an image of YHWH to be bowed to by any devout believer?

It is possible that King Hezekiah actually did not know that the Nehushtan was a sacred object, and possibly a physical representation of YHWH. Because the Hebrew canon as a whole was not in general circulation at that time, it is just possible that Hezekiah had the Nehushtan destroyed, not knowing its story of origin, not understanding it to be the image of YHWH, and writing it off as an unhelpful vestige of the old ways, nothing better than an idol.

However, the fact that Jewish believers worshipped the Nehushtan, strongly suggests that the people at large knew the story around it and understood what it was. If the people reverencing the Bronze Dragon knew it to be a likeness of YHWH, surely the king and Azariah, his high priestly advisor, would also know. If that is the case, then we have to view Hezekiah's decision to have it destroyed in a totally different light. In that case Hezekiah and Azariah's action was not a clean-up of what they saw as idolatry. Rather it was an attempt to hide from the public the knowledge of what YHWH actually looked like. Given that Hezekiah and Azariah's agenda was to elevate the worship of YHWH and to present him as a transcendent God, it is conceivable that the destruction of the Nehushtan was part of a deliberate and radical rebranding of YHWH himself.

In a later generation, King Hezekiah's great-grandson, King Josiah embarked on a major reconstruction of the high priestly Temple of Solomon in Jerusalem. During the renovations, Hilkiah the High Priest stumbled across something unfamiliar. It was a book, titled *The Book of the Laws of YHWH*. Nobody quite knows what this mysterious book comprised. Could it be the book of Deuteronomy? Was it all five books of the Torah? Whatever it was, II Kings presents it as the entire basis of Josiah's rebranding of Judaism. Josiah regarded his royal reforms as a reassertion of the divine kingship of Yahweh and, by extension, the divine right to rule of the kings of Jerusalem and the high priests of the Jerusalem Temple. The problem is that whether the mysterious book in question was Deuteronomy or the Pentateuch, what we are looking at in the time of King Josiah is the earlier, unredacted version of these books, the versions with all the elohim still showing. The Book of the Laws of YHWH included undisguised narratives of elohim, Elyon the Captain, Shaddai the Destroyer, CH-CH the Dragon, Asherah, Baal, Dagon, the moloch child-sacrifices, and the whole kaleidoscopic memory of the seba hassamayim. Far from Judaic monotheism it was the memory of the whole array of sky armies, otherwise known as *elohim*, who governed humanity in the deep past.

If it is true that young King Josiah was eager to present the *Book of the Laws of Yahweh* as his divine mandate for reinventing Judaism, then when Hilkiah presented the book to Shaphan the royal scribe, both men have quickly recognised serious problems within the text. They would have understood that this proto-canon was not the manifesto for a monotheist theocracy that the king might wish it to be. Whether it was Deuteronomy only, or a summary or extract of the books of the Pentateuch, the resurfaced *Book of the Laws of Yahweh* would have been a ticking time-bomb for Josiah's hope of a neat and tidy theocracy. It was only a matter of time before the high priest and royal scribe would need to make a decision as to whether these scriptures would need to be *"lost"* a second time, or whether they should be entirely re-written. The broad consensus among today's academic Biblical scholars is that within decades of Josiah's elevation of the *Book of the Laws of Yahweh*, an urgent and radical re-write became the order of the day.

But before we get too angry with King Josiah for obscuring Judaism's memories of paleocontact through the reforms he initiated, we should take note that when he became king, Josiah was a boy of no more than eight years old. Was he really the one in the driver's seat, directing this process of historical revisionism? The fact of his age suggests that other figures were probably in play in this critical moment. To have a purely ceremonial king of only eight years old may not be a problem. Some might even consider it cute. However, a king with real power who is only eight years old is quite another matter. The accession of a boy as king creates a crisis, a nightmare for some and an opportunity for others. This is the way it was when Josiah was crowned king.

By way of comparison, there was a boy of a similar age to Josiah, who in the sixteenth century inherited the English throne. Edward VI was no more than nine years old when he succeeded his father Henry VIII as king of England. Upon his accession, Edward immediately found himself supported by the patriarchs of two powerful families. These were families who had been deeply invested in the religious and political reforms initiated by the old king. Edward's young age provided the patriarchs of these two families, the Seymours and the Dudleys, with an opportunity to get a grip on national policy, accelerate the reforms and push them even further, while simultaneously anchoring their own positions in the kingdom as the powers behind the throne. I have no doubt that what happened to the nine-year-old Edward also happened to eight-year-old Josiah, and that Josiah's handlers recognised a similar opportunity.

Hilkiah, was the patriarch of the Jerusalem High Priestly family. Tasked with the young king's spiritual guidance, he and Shaphan, the Royal Scribe, now found themselves in a position to thoroughly reform the beliefs and practices of the Jewish people, monotheizing their religion, legitimizing the Jerusalem royal court, and elevating the Jerusalem temple. But this was more than a matter of centralization of power. It was a party-political victory

104

which effected a profound alteration of Jewish religion, transforming what Jews believed, how they related to the universe and what they believed about God.

By the time Josiah set about his reforms he had been under the continual guidance of Hilkiah the High Priest and Shaphan the Royal Scribe for eighteen years. Both men were priests of YHWH. Perhaps today it is easy to forget that Judaism did in fact have other kinds of priest to offer. For instance, Josiah's grandfather King Manasseh had a temple built to Asherah, staffed by a royal cadre of priests devoted to Asherah. Let the fact sink in that the priests of Asherah were Jewish priests. Their royal commission was to maintain a cultural memory of paleocontact of the positive kind. Similarly, King Manasseh's grandfather Ahaz had temples constructed in commemoration of other entities *"on every high hill and under every green tree."* Each of these temples required their own cadres of priests – priests of Baal and priests of Asherah. Similarly, King Solomon's installations required priests of Asherah and priests of Chemosh.

Once again the redactors had a tricky task on their hands. Their commentary on this history had to do three contradictory things:

- elevate the YHWHist credentials of the Jewish kingly line
- divinize the one particular elohim called YHWH
- demonize all the other elohim of the Seba Hassamayim enthusiastically commemorated by the Jewish kings

For these reasons the redactors of II Kings and II Chronicles were careful to layer fierce condemnation over the top of their report of royal devotion to the diversity of elohim of the Seba Hassamayim.

Their solution was simple and bold. It was the wives' fault. Solomon's commemoration of Asherah and Chemosh could be put down to the inevitable problems thrown up by marrying a foreign woman. Enough said. Scapegoat the foreigner! Blame it on the wife! No further explanation was needed.

In a similar vein, being anxious to destroy any possibility of a reader approving of King Ahaz, the redactors of II Kings and II Chronicles assert that this king's diversion from YHWHism was so extreme as to have led him into an appalling practice of child-sacrifice. Once again the narrators explain that the chief factor in bringing this Jewish king so low was the tarnishing presence of a foreign wife - the charismatic and beautiful Lebanese woman, Jezebel. Bloody foreigner!

So this was the fix: It was foreign wives who lured their royal husbands into erecting standing stones, building temples and commissioning priesthoods devoted to the commemoration of paleocontact. Watch out for foreigners, and especially beware of foreign women! You get the idea? Given that this overall explanation of non-YHWHist kings, queens and priests was written up by a rival priesthood, the YHWHist priesthood of Jerusalem, I think it is fair to ask if this damning report of the various other priesthoods of Judaism is an unbiased one.

To say that Josiah grew up under the influence of the YHWHist High Priest, Hilkiah, is to point out that he grew up with a constant reinforcement of a YHWHist party perspective over and against all the other Jewish priesthoods scattered throughout Judea, receiving tithes and offerings, teaching the people, and honouring the memory of other powerful ones. This was the party political perspective of the voice, periodically leaning into the young king's ear, and whispering, *"Sir, I have identified yet another serious threat to your majesty's control over the nation. Would you like me to take care of it?"*

Josiah's *"Yes,"* to his High Priestly advisor meant the demolition of the temples of Judea, leaving only the Jerusalem temple remaining. It meant the destruction of standing stones, commemorating the places throughout Judea in which their Hebrew ancestors had first met their advanced visitors. It meant confiscating figurines and breaking off their heads so they could never again be used in the commemoration of Asherah. And it meant sending in the Jerusalem Guard to destroy the carvings of the Seba Hassamyim so that in the future the only cultural recollection of the ancient airborne armies would be the memory of YHWH. These changes transformed what Jewish people believed about themselves, God, and the world around them. It centralized the nation's political power and wealth in Jerusalem, simultaneously anchoring the power of the high priestly family within the fabric of the nation. What had been one of many priesthoods was now the only priesthood. This shift in power was soon to prove quite strategic.

Within twenty-three years of King Josiah's death from a battle-wound at the age of thirty-eight, there would be no Jewish monarchy left and the first Jerusalem Temple would lie in ruins, sacked by the Babylonian army. The maintenance of Jewish identity under the power of Babylon, its physical centres of power gone and its monarchy ended, would seem an almost impossible challenge. However, with the tribes of Israel now conceived of as a YHWHist theocracy, there was a way forward. The king and the royal court may be gone, the grand edifice of the Jerusalem temple courts may have been demolished, but the priestly tribe and the family of the High Priest remained and could continue to guide the affairs of the nation through these incredibly testing times. What had been the power behind the throne a generation before was now the only power within Jewish society.

In effect, the ritual reforms under Josiah marked the beginning of a silent coup, a subtle shift of power, which moved the ground under the feet of Judaism, subtly morphing it from an ethnic or tribal grouping into an organised religion. Given the loss of the nation's geopolitical footing in the early C6thBCE it was a strategic and important shift which ensured the survival of Judaism as a force in the world. Had this shift not occurred YHWHism would not have survived the Babylonian exile and captivity. If the silent coup had not happened and the power to define Jewish identity had been left to the kings it would have been a different story, because out of the four Jewish kings who followed Josiah only the first, Josiah's eldest son, was a YHWHist. The final three Jewish kings were not YHWHists. They followed the old ways. They were paleocontact people.

Following the silent coup, the loss of the Jewish monarchy was an opportunity for the High Priesthood to have free reign in defining YHWHism and making it the bedrock of Jewish society. In the mid C5thBCE another significant steppingstone presented itself. A new temple in Jerusalem was completed. Commissioned by the Persian King Cyrus, to allow his Jewish subjects their freedom of religion, the temple ultimately became known as the Temple of Herod, since it was he who took the credit for finally completing it. With the inauguration of the new temple, the patience of the High Priestly family could now be rewarded.

A senior member of the High Priestly family by the name of Ezra now undertook to establish YHWHism as the basis of Jewish religious life, re-centred on the newly restored Jerusalem. Emulating the reforming decree of King Josiah two centuries before, Ezra presented the people with a holy text to serve as the bedrock of their religious nation. The book was called *"The Book of Moses."* Clearly this new sacred text was something different to *"The Book of the Laws of Yahweh."* And this difference has led some scholars to argue that Ezra may in fact be the scribe responsible for completing the work of reform commenced by Hilkiah and Shaphan, two centuries before, by producing what we

108

now call the Pentateuch or the Torah. Personally, I share the broad consensus among Biblical scholars that *The Book of Moses* had in fact already been completed during the Babylonian captivity of the previous century. The establishment of the second temple was simply the opportunity for the High Priestly family to re-attach Jewish religion to YHWHism on the basis of a sacred and immutable text.

Whether he was the final redactor or simply the redactors' champion, Ezra personifies the continuity of the priestly elite through all the turbulence of the intervening generations. He was closely related to Seriah, the final High Priest of the first Jerusalem temple (Solomon's Temple) and to Joshua, the first High Priest of the second temple (Herod's Temple.) He is part of an unbroken family line and an unbroken scribal tradition serving the YHWHist ideals and reforming agenda of their C7thBCE ancestors. *(The Bible references this sequence of events in the books II Chronicles and Ezra.)*

I have gone into depth to explain why. Why the change in Judaism from commemoration of paleocontact to YHWHism and law-keeping? The question now is, *"How?!"* How did Ezra's predecessors produce *The Book of Moses?* What redactions had to be done to the *Book of the Laws of Yahweh* and to the other ancient literature recognized as sacred Hebrew texts to turn them into a coherent canon and a basis for YHWHist religion?

Most fundamentally, if YHWH was to be seen as a divine figurehead, he himself would need a radical rebrand. In their day King Josiah and his great-grandfather King Hezekiah had clearly wanted to redeem the name of YHWH to serve as their sacred name for a transcendent deity, a divine figurehead befitting a modern, enlightened, monotheistic faith. This was how Ezra's *Book of Moses* presented YHWH. However, the intervening generations of priests and scribes had a Herculean task before

109

them. Simply airbrushing over the scriptures' earlier usage of the name YHWH was not something to be easily achieved. The countless physical, animal, and draconian references to YHWH, are scattered so liberally throughout the Hebrew canon that they could not all be removed. We know this because they are still visible. For instance, in the book of Job, the writer describes two terrifying beasts, the behemoth and the leviathan. The behemoth operates on land and the leviathan operates under water. Of the leviathan the YHWH character says,

"Can you pull in the leviathan with a fish-hook or tie down his tongue with a rope? Can you put a cord through his nose, or pierce his jaw with a hook? Will he keep begging you for mercy...[and] agree to be your slave for life?" (Job 41)

The description of the leviathan extends to its limbs, graceful body, a jaw ringed with fearsome teeth, a scaly back that looks like rows of shields, smoke from its nostrils and breath that, like a giant version of the Bombardier beetle, can ignite as fire. It certainly sounds fearful, but why would YHWH compare his own prowess with that of a dragon-like animal? The book of Job's description of the behemoth is similar.

"It feeds on grass like an ox. What strength it has in its loins! What power it has in the muscles of its belly! Its tail sways like a cedar. The sinews of its thighs are close-knit. Its bones are tubes of bronze. Its limbs are like rods of iron." (Job 40)

And if it isn't clear enough in the English, yes that language is full of oblique references to the behemoth's genitals. Once again, to raise the obvious question, if YHWH was Almighty God or a transcendent spiritual being, why would he describe his own power by comparing himself with a big-balled beast? There is no evidence to suggest that behemoth and leviathan were well-known symbology for cultural enemies or the powerful ones of rival nations. So it's not a metaphorical point score. Everything about the description of behemoth and leviathan is of flesh and bone beasts which were too powerful for human beings to stand up against. That is how the writer or redactor of Job presents YHWH. And these are not the only places where the physical attributes of YHWH are referenced.

In Psalm 18 and II Samuel 22 King David gives a detailed physical description of *"YHWH my Powerful One."* He describes smoke arising from YHWH's *ap* – a word which means nostrils or snout – and fire coming from YHWH's mouth. He shoots arrows and bolts of lightning. And the blast of breath from his *ap* is sufficient to *"expose the valleys of the sea"* and *"lay bare the foundations of the earth."*

Now, at this point it would be fair to ask if this draconian imagery was originally intended not for a reptilian creature but a terrifying piece of ancient technology. We could ask the identical question when the same text tells us that YHWH mounted a *kruv* and flew on it. Is the writer describing YHWH's use of an animal or a vehicle? When we come to the Hebrew word *ruach* in a later chapter we will see that technological readings of these intriguing verses might have some merit. For a point of comparison, in the Mayan stories of the Progenitors in the Popol Vuh, there are texts which appear to describe craft, containing detailed references to metallic hulls, flashing lights and emissions of smoke and fire, lighting up the night sky. In one place in the Popol Vuh the Progenitors are described in animal-like terms, in another they are described as finely skilled scientists, what we would call genetic engineers, and in yet another the same names are applied to their mysterious flying craft. Is it possible that we have a similar spectrum in the dragon-references of the Bible, with some referring to living entities and others referring to their craft? Did our ancestors describe the craft as animals because they had no technological framework by which to interpret what they were seeing?

Whichever it is, throughout the Hebrew scriptures, the length of YHWH's *ap* and the smoke that arises from it, YHWH's wings and flight feathers, his mighty voice, the blast of his breath, the thunderous sound, and the issue of fire from his mouth are all associated with YHWH's destructive powers. Clearly this particular **CH-CH** entity and his technology constituted a power not to be messed with. Accordingly, Isaiah 42 summarizes the general dynamic of YHWH's leadership like this: *"[The people] refused to walk in his ways nor were they obedient to his laws. So [YHWH] poured upon them fury from his ap, which is his great power in battle, and set them all on fire until there was nothing left of them."*

Whether craft or creature, the very concrete nature of this powerful, destructive thing is referenced further in the deutero-canonical book of *Bel and the Dragon*, to be found in the Septuagint. In this story the narrator mocks the people of Israel's rivals, the Babylonians, who claim to serve an entity every bit as impressive as YHWH. This entity, so say the Babylonians, is a dragon, whom they keep in the deepest recesses of an enormous sequence of layered tents, shrouded in darkness and smoke. Every day the Babylonians provide their resident powerful one with vast supplies of edible offerings.

However, the Jewish Prince, Daniel, happens to know that this arrangement is all an elaborate hoax. He knows because he has already killed the Babylonian dragon, as recounted in a previous story. He knows that the constant supplies of edible offerings intended for the dragon are in reality being consumed by the seventy priests and their families. The embarrassing truth is that the Babylonians' innermost tent is empty. The priests have been faking it all this time. By contrast the priests of Israel are not faking it. The smokiest, darkest recess in their mighty sequence of tents houses a real, living entity. YHWH's priests are not consuming the continual edible offerings demanded by YHWH. Their people's tribute is going to a real, live powerful one and his name is YHWH. That is the punchline of *Bel and the Dragon*.

Just in case you think that this deutero-canonical story might be no more than a piece of fan fiction which has somehow got the wrong end of the stick, this exact same pattern of tribute to YHWH is unpacked in detail in the book of Numbers. Moses has just prosecuted and won a significant military campaign against the neighbouring Midianites. So he is happy, but only until he finds out that his soldiers have killed all the men, but mercifully spared the lives of the women and children. On making this discovery, Moses is furious. Instantly he demands to know why all these women and children have been left alive. Moses is emphatic as he spits out the order. *"Kill the women and kill all the boys. Leave only the virgin girls alive. You soldiers can keep them for yourselves."* (Numbers 31)

If that weren't horrific enough, the devil is in the detail. The spoils from this battle are highly significant and the narrator takes some time to enumerate precisely what went to whom.

- The total booty is 675,000 sheep and goats, 72,000 head of cattle, 61,000 donkeys, and 32,000 virgin girls.
- Half of this is then given to the soldiers.
- Of the half of the spoils set aside for the community, Moses takes 2% for YHWH's priests.
- 675 sheep and goats, 72 cattle, 61 donkeys, and 32 virgin girls are then set aside for YHWH and are entrusted to the priest Eleazer.
- YHWH also gets 420 pounds of gold.

Note that this makes very clear that YHWH's share cannot be understood to mean the spoils for the priests. They are two different portions. Unlike the fraudulent priests of Bel and the Dragon, YHWH's priests are not secretly eating all YHWH's food. Here's the relevant detail:

- The priests receive 6,750 sheep and goats to share, while YHWH gets 675 <u>for himself</u>.
- The priests receive 720 head of cattle while YHWH gets 72 cattle <u>for himself.</u>

What does it tell us that YHWH commanded his humans to keep him continually supplied with gold, edible offerings of beef and lamb, and virgin girls <u>for himself</u>?

Within the Biblical narratives we can see that the pattern of tribute paid to YHWH parallels the tribute of other people groups towards their powerful ones, Bel and the Dragon being just one example. However, there is a far wider context for the pattern of tribute paid to YHWH. All around the world ancestral narratives concerning dragons tell us that they continually put upon their humans to keep them supplied with those exact same things. It seems that dragons all around the world like gold, beef, lamb and virgin girls. The YHWH narrative, exemplified in Numbers 31, fits that pattern precisely.

At this point, you might ask me, what difference does it make? What difference does it make to us today whether Numbers 31 is talking about God or about a dragon? Why should you or I care whether YHWH looked like the Nehushtan or if he looked like something else? Don't we have more important things to worry about in the twenty-first century? The difference lies in what these ancient writers are trying to tell us about the world around us. Generations of authors and scribes have given their lives' work to curating these memories for future generations. What was it they wanted us to know? I believe that the answer lies in a pivot in the story of human development. It has to do with politics, power, and the spectre of covert layers of government. All these messages and more flow from a decisive moment in the Biblical story in which the power of the dragon is finally confronted. To understand how and why, I invite you to join me on the west coast of Africa where an ancestor of mine played his part in just such a pivotal moment in the history of the Gold Coast, what today we call Ghana.

Chapter Eight

Despots, Vested Objects and The Great Coup

Cape Coast, The Gold Coast, West Africa – 1948

"The streets and squares are thronged with students. Some have organised the demonstration and many more besides are watching, cheering the demonstrators on, while still more crowd into the public spaces to see how the authorities will respond. The atmosphere is buoyant. The mood of the whole country is shifting. Today's demonstration is a show of solidarity with the six executives of the United Gold Coast Convention. Just last week they were arrested for the crime of campaigning for our country to be allowed democratic government."

"We want democracy. We want our national sovereignty returned. And we would like to extend an invitation to His Majesty George VI to call his deputies and officials and soldiers out of our country and back to Britain. Instead, the King's officers have put the six executives in prison for treason. Even so the mood on the street is high. We support the United Gold Coast Convention. And there have been no more arrests today. No, that will be tomorrow."

Our local narrator is of course correct. The academic authorities of St Augustine's College and Mfantsipim School, the source of today's academic demonstrators, will wait till the crowds have gone home. Tomorrow they will expel the one hundred and fifty students involved in today's activities. They will also fire a number of teachers for gross sedition against His Majesty. This may seem a harsh response. Yet what our narrator from 1948 could not possibly know was that the response of the crown's forces in Ghana was positively mild when compared with the horrors to be exacted on the people of Kenya by the time Ghana had finally won her independence less than a decade later. What played out in Kenya was a kind of warfare on humanity which could have been modelled on great sections of the Biblical story. In the paragraphs ahead I am going to share a few thumbnail sketches of colonial governance to provide some points of reference for understanding the dynamics of YHWHist rule in the Biblical accounts.

The twentieth century was a pivot in the history of empires. Indeed, some of the ugliest moments in colonial history would play out in other countries during that period. Gunpoint governance often reaches its most brutal extreme as a regime loses its grip on power. Occupation often begins when an imperial power approaches an independent country full of useful resources, or occupying some strategic position. The imperial power introduces itself with an offer of protection, couched in terms like these: *"We will domicile a major military force in your country. This will be of great benefit to your country's safety in the world and will equip your government to better manage any problems you may be having with insurgents. In return you will give us your sovereignty."*

Of course, the subtext is, *"You're going to need to be part of somebody's empire – ours or our opponents'. Take your pick."* The occupied country then has to calculate what it hopes will be the lesser of two or three evils. In due course the occupying army proves that it is really there to serve the interests of the colonizers far above the needs of the colonized. Gradually the entire economic and political system of the country is transformed. Firstly, the colonizing power creates systems of monopolies over products and industries, then issues and requires licenses for access to land, resources and trade. By these means, access to wealth can then be controlled and redistributed on the basis of loyalty to the new regime. At this point a farmer no longer has the right to use his own river frontage or rainwater, is no longer allowed to sow his own crops, or to farm his own land. Through measures like these, along with taxation of property already owned, the traditional economic base of the population can be removed. Abolishing traditional land rights, and reducing the people's wealth, health and security creates a population without a surplus of time and energy. The people become anxious, dependent, and sick. Far more manageable.

Disloyalty to the colonizer, now called *"sedition,"* can be met with the seizure of a family's property, which can then be reassigned to a family loyal to the colonizer. The dispossessed family must then be separated, husband from wife, and parents from children, to be interred in separate death camps, where rebels are be hanged and only those willing to show loyalty to the colonisers are fed. Foods and medicines will be supplied as a reward for compliance and loyalty. It will be withheld from everybody else.

Those who survive starvation in the camps can then be put to forced labour. Any leaders of movements disloyal to the colonizers must be publicly tortured and executed in large numbers, parents in front of their children, children in front of their parents. The executions and torture must be dramatic and done in public in order to send a clear signal to the wider population. The message is that it is better to love the colonizer than to resist. Pleas for mercy to the emperor, king or foreign power must fall on deaf ears, and must be seen to fall on deaf ears.

This horrific vision is not a hypothetical, nor is it a generalization. If only.

At this point you may be doing some mental arithmetic. Am I talking about empire X, Y, or Z?" Is this the story of country A, B, or C? Is this about President D or Queen E? The fact that these are three legitimate questions reflects how widespread this approach to colonization has been. These patterns are not the eccentric choices of one aberrant leader. They are the very fabric of colonialism. But to answer the question, specifically, every single measure I have just detailed was meted out by the military forces loyal to King George VI's imperial successor Queen Elizabeth II in the terminal years of her reign over the country of Kenya. Hers were the royal ears turned deaf to desperate pleas for mercy for the lives of sons and fathers as her loyal officers dispensed capital punishment on a truly horrendous scale. In fact many historians calculate that, as a means of checking a country's movement towards democracy and self-governance, this was the most extensive prosecution of capital punishment orders on record. But, whatever the empire, be it British, Dutch, Spanish, Portuguese, Danish, Byzantine, Mongol, or Roman, the dynamics of colonial governance differs very little from age to age, and it was something well known to our distant ancestors. The reason I have taken the time to detail these means of colonization is to show how our Hebrew forbears foreshadowed every single methodology I have itemised in the narratives which became the Bible.

This geopolitical aspect becomes clear the moment we recognize that in the Bible we are reading stories of paleocontact. When understood as the memories of non-human powers ruling over colonies of our ancestors in the deep past, their colonialist devices stand out in clear relief and are instantly recognisable. One of the most interesting examples of this can be found in the book of I

Samuel. This book describes a moment similar to the Cape Coast demonstrations which led to Ghanaian independence. The pivot point occurs in chapter 8. Here we see the people of Israel gathering with their tribal leaders to confront YHWH and throw off his direct rule. Henceforward they intend to be governed by one of their own. *"Human leaders for human society!"* According to I Samuel, this revolutionary confrontation was sparked by corruption, the abuse of YHWH's delegated powers by his unaccountable vice-regent, the prophet Samuel, and Samuel's three sons. Initially the people appeal to YHWH against his corrupt deputies, to find that their pleas are falling on deaf ears. In fact, YHWH regards the people's criticism of Samuel's administration as an affront to his own authority. So what if his vice-regents were corrupt and unjust?! So what if this was the exact same corruption the previous generation had suffered under the previous administration?! So what if these problems were never addressed?! How was that any of the people's business? So what if YHWH's deputies were compassionless and corrupt?! How did that implicate YHWH himself?

When the moment of confrontation comes, YHWH responds by sending Samuel into the public square, to front up to the baying crowd and issue a strongly-worded warning. If the people are determined not to cooperate with the rule of YHWH, and appoint a human king instead, this, he says, is what the people can expect from a human king:

"He will separate your families. He will seize your boys and use them as soldiers to fight in his armies. He will force your sons into labour on his own farms and set them to work in his armaments factories. He will take your daughters from you and turn them into his slaves."

"He will take the best of your, crop-yielding farms, the best of your olive groves and vineyards, and re-assign them as rewards for his deputies and those who loyally serve him."

"He will impose tax on the fruit of your labours, your wine and grain, and what he takes from you he will supply to his own officers, and servants."

"He will take your young men, your male and female servants and your donkeys and make them work on his own properties."

"He will tax the property you already own, your goods and livestock. In these ways he will reduce you to a life of servitude."

"On that day you will cry out to YHWH for mercy, and he will not hear you."

Does any of that sound familiar? These patterns of colonization, where the colonizer's power is built on injustice, theft, terror, and violence, are as old as the hills. And YHWH knew these patterns from the inside out. Over time, the Bible's narratives reveal that YHWH would ultimately employ every single one of those tactics.

The dual theme of *"I will protect you, and I will punish you,"* is the dynamic of any colonizing power, when establishing its new relationship. It is that same psychopathic double-speak we noted before which says, *"No-one can protect you from others like I can, and no-one can protect you from me."* The same dynamic can be seen in YHWH's relationship with the people of Israel. On the one hand we have YHWH's words in Genesis 18: *"I will bless whoever blesses you and curse whoever curses you."* On the other hand, we have the words of Isaiah 42, *"[The people] refused to walk in his ways nor were they obedient to his laws. So [YHWH]*

poured upon [his own people] fury from his nose [ap] his great
power in battle and set all the people's bodies on fire until there
was nothing left of them."

In this way warfare was a device by which YHWH could demonstrate both his authority and his power. It was a constant reminder of who he was and of the place of obedience which belonged to his people. It also kept his people dependent. By contrast, back in the days of Abraham, the patriarch's household and people had lived largely at peace with their neighbours through a culture of negotiating peace treaties and forging alliances. Whereas, under the rule of YHWH, Abraham's descendants found themselves conscripted into continual warfare, living their lives on high alert. On numerous occasions YHWH tells his deputies specifically never to make peace treaties and alliances but rather to pursue total war, leaving behind no human survivors and no cultural artefacts. If you have ever wondered at the financial priority given by certain countries to warfare overseas over and against health, prosperity and wellbeing at home, look no further than the annals of YHWH for a prototype. Consequently, poor-and-anxious was the general condition of YHWH's people for a period of forty years, during which the people lived as dispossessed nomads in the Sinai desert.

It was throughout this unhappy period that the people were sustained by emergency daily rations of manna – a word which means *"what is it?"* Whatever it was, it wouldn't last more than a day before spoiling. This system of rations kept the people in a perpetual state of anxiety and dependence, just surviving. As we saw in a previous chapter, when the people became sick and tired of this regimen and complained, YHWH deployed his munitions against his own people. Only those willing to kowtow would be spared the effects. This is not so different to the targeted use of starvation, and the targeted distribution of medications exploited in the British death camps in twentieth century Kenya.

Torture and the spectacle of pleas for mercy falling on deaf ears also figure in the YHWH stories. King Saul, King David, and King Ahaziah all experienced these devices in their personal relationships with YHWH. None of these men were rebels, agitating for independence. They were YHWH's own kings. Yet they shouldn't have been surprised by their treatment. At the institution of the monarchy, YHWH's spokesperson Samuel declared in advance that future generations of Israelites could expect a deaf ear from YHWH should they ever wish to turn to him for mercy. This is an irony of the highest degree given that Samuel's name means *"The Powerful One Hears,"* although, of course, there are two ways of reading that, one as a message of comfort, the other a warning of *Big Brother*!

The moments of YHWH's most disturbing actions are recognizably moments in which YHWH feels his own grip on power is waning. For instance, it is when YHWH's successor King Saul runs a war more mercifully than the way YHWH would have done that YHWH deposes him, afflicting him with a spiritual parasite which ultimately drives the king to insanity and suicide. Having got rid of Saul, YHWH installs David who does well for a while, right up until II Samuel 24. This chapter recalls a moment when YHWH realizes that David is laying the mental groundwork for questioning his battle orders. David is now old and wise enough that he only wants to fight winnable wars. To this end he has to know the exact scale of his armies. So he counts his troops. An obvious an uncontroversial thing to do, you might think. To the power behind the throne, however, this is unacceptable. The only factor in whether David should send his troops to war should be YHWH's say-so. So, for this insolence, YHWH executes seventy-thousand of his own infantry. YHWH is sending the signal that no diminution of his authority will be tolerated. *"You do not think for yourself! You do not even think of questioning orders or making up your own mind!"* That's the message. The seventy thousand men killed were not rebels. They were his own loyal soldiers, and the offending action was nothing to do with them.

A similar example can be found in YHWH's relationship with King Ahazaiah at a time when he is mortally injured after an accident and is lying on his deathbed. Ahaziah sends for the medical expertise of a neighbouring elohim, hoping for a prognosis. When YHWH learns that Ahaziah is consulting with an elohim other than himself, he pronounces a death sentence over Ahaziah, being outraged that any other powerful one would be considered a better medical expert than himself.

In these moments with Saul, David and Ahaziah, YHWH can see that his wisdom and wishes are beginning to be considered and compared. This is not the spirit of unquestioning obedience that YHWH wants. His response is a heightening of terror and violence. Thus, even in the governance of his own people of Israel, YHWH displays the classic pattern in which it is the waning period of a colonizer's stronghold that sees the brutality of gunpoint governance taken to its extreme.

By contrast to this rather bleak picture, back in 1948 our Ghanaian narrator is feeling optimistic for the future of his country. As he surveys the public show of solidarity in Cape Coast, he can see in real time the fundamental shift in the mathematics of governance. A colonising power depends on a mathematical formula that runs like this: *"To persecute one oppresses thousands."* That's how it works. An example will be made of some or other trouble-maker,

125

and his treatment will be so brutal that no onlooker will ever want to risk sharing the trouble-maker's horrendous fate. However, if the mathematics pivots the other way, that's when the colonizers should know their days of power are numbered. If you persecute one and see a thousand stand up and say, *"You cannot treat my brother that way,"* then you can be confident that your tenure as a despot is on borrowed time. 1948 is the mathematical pivot in Britain's affairs in Ghana. Six campaigners for democracy have been arrested and hundreds have turned out in solidarity. The dynamic has reversed. This is why our narrator in Cape Coast is buoyed with confidence in the days following the student demonstration. This really is a climatic shift.

"Today on the Gold Coast we are optimistic British rule here is on a stopwatch, and we are counting down to zero. People are coming together to say, 'No to the empire," and 'No to foreign rule!'

"We are seeing a new beginning. The popular academic, Kwame Nkrumah, has responded to the expulsions from St Augustine's College and *Mfantsipim School by founding a new school with his own money. It will become The Ghana National College. To create a new faculty, Kwame has gathered his four most valued political comrades in the world of education – three from St. Augustine's College and one from Mfantsipim School."*

Incidentally, I want to let you know that I have a personal stake in this story. Among Nkrumah's committee of five, the comrade from Mfantsipim was my Great Uncle, the late Henry *"Kofi"* Sackeyfio. The school will become a rallying point and powerbase for Ghanaian independence. Within a decade Kwame Nkrumah will become the first Prime Minister and later the first President of a democratic and independent Ghana. The liberation of Ghana after nearly one hundred and forty years of British rule is a moment of great pride for the people of Ghana and for that whole side of my family.

"My family are Ashanti people. And in Ghana the people all know that the British military has never ever succeeded in claiming the Golden Throne of the Ashanti people! Without the Golden Throne how could the British governors ever expect to remain here? So we have every reason to be hopeful."

Why is this Ashanti detail important? What is a Golden Throne? Why does it matter? And how does it connect with elohim, Elyon, or YHWH in the annals of Jewish history? Our travels in the coming pages will reveal that these questions are ultimately connected with esoteric technology buried in the Levant, Guatemala, and Mexico. We will find other answers in secret emblems carefully incorporated into the paraphernalia of the coronation of King Charles III in 2023. But before we make those journeys we must first make our way north, to the southern shores of Loch Etive in Argyll, Scotland, to commemorate the passing of a local hero – a retired criminal lawyer with an intriguing back-story.

October 3ʳᵈ 2022 - Scotland

It's in all the papers and on every newsfeed. Ian Hamilton has died at the ripe old age of ninety-seven. One of Scotland's most respected QCs, he has served the country for decades as an eminent criminal lawyer. The whole country will honour him and mark his passing, and a film has already been made to tell his story, with the actor Robert Carlyle taking the part of Ian Hamilton. Why?

Because, as a young law student, Ian Hamilton embarked on one of the most extraordinary and daring raids in British history. With fellow students, Alan Stuart, Gavin Vernon and Kay Matheson, Ian made the long journey from Glasgow to London, and in particular to Westminster Abbey, the place where English Kings and Queens have been crowned for a thousand years. Having opened a side-door of the abbey with a crowbar, his comrades entered the darkened building and located a large wooden chair. From underneath the seat they managed to prise a 336 pounds (152 kilos) block of sandstone which, with great difficulty and in the face of many challenges, they smuggled all the way back to Scotland. Having evaded pursuing police and now arriving safely across the border, the four conspirators escort the heavy stone to Arbroath Abbey, where they quietly leave it at the high altar, in the sanctuary of the church. It is Christmas Day 1950.

Why would a student of law risk arrest and all kinds of punishment for 336 pounds of sandstone? And why did its arrival in Scotland spark celebrations in Scottish streets, and in Westminster foment government fears of a Scottish uprising? Many years later Hamilton reflected on the theft of the stone. *"Independence is now inevitable. The stone...transcends politics. Regardless of our political views, Scots recognize that there is something that binds us together."*

What was this all about? What would a man destined to be a QC, a man of honour like Ian Hamilton, be doing raiding Westminster Abbey and outrunning the police? And what was it about that block of sandstone that was sufficient to spark celebrations in Scotland and fears of revolution in England? The answer is that the sandstone block in question is Scotland's most sacred vested object. Prior to 1296 when the English seized it from Scotland and smuggled it to Westminster, the stone block had been used for centuries in the coronation of Scottish kings. Once in Westminster King Edward I had it built into the coronation seat. Suffice it to say, it was a significant piece of stone. Moreover, the place where Ian Hamilton and his comrades left the stone was also significant. The High Altar of Arbroath Abbey was the place where the Scottish barons, the clan leaders, had once gathered, to join their names in assignation to Scotland's declaration of independence on April 6th, 1320. This declaration was then sent to Pope John XXII for him to acknowledge and defend their sovereignty. To the kings of England, who since the time of Edward II had used it for their own coronations, the stolen sandstone embodies the right to rule over the lands of Scotland. That is the power and authority with which this block of sandstone has been vested. Its name is the *Stone of Scone*, otherwise known as the *Stone of Destiny*.

This exciting episode is only a snapshot of the Stone of Destiny's long life. The English saw the stone as an object vested with authority to rule because the Scottish did. Why did the Scottish people see the stone that way? According to accounts written in the fourteenth and sixteenth centuries, before Scottish kings first used it for their coronations, the Stone of Destiny had been used to crown Simon Breck as the King of Ireland. The Scots had then brought it with them when they migrated from Ireland to Scotland. Simon Breck's royal ancestor, Prince Gathelus, was a son of the Greek King Cecrops, and he was said to have brought the sandstone to Ireland via Spain and Egypt, having originally sourced it in Syria. It was, so he believed, part of the pedestal of the Ark of the Covenant – the ancient, vested object and throne of the Kings of Israel. The builders of the Ark of the Covenant, so the legend goes, had sourced this stone at Bethel, a part of the ancient site built by Jacob, the patriarch of the Twelve Tribes of Israel, to commemorate his encounter with the mysterious powerful ones, whom he saw arriving from and departing into space.

However few or many of those details may be facts, this legend, which is centuries old, illustrates historic ideas about the importance and nature of vested objects. It also roots the power and significance of the Stone of Destiny in one of Judaism's earliest stories of ET contact. But why would a Scottish King want to tie his right to rule to a vested object connected with the regime of YHWH? What did they believe the Ark of the Covenant was, that they would want a piece of it? And what was the Ark of the Covenant in reality? Furthermore, why would an object vested with ET associations have any bearing over the right to govern Scotland?

As I write, it is the year of the coronation of King Charles III in Westminster. For that moment the Scottish Stone of Destiny was loaned to Westminster Abbey for the ceremony and re-fitted to Edward II's chair, to entitle him to rule over Scotland. It is not the only vested object in play as part of the ceremony. The crown is a vested object. So is the orb and the sceptre. So is the gold from this colony, the diamond from another, the opal from this colony, a sapphire from another, all embedded into the monarch's headwear. When that headwear passes from one royal head to another, so does the wealth it represents, and with it the power and authority to rule. As we saw in a previous chapter, the grand vestments of church and state carry symbolism from ancient Rome, Israel, Persia and Babylon. The use of these emblems communicates a strong message about the continuity and impregnability, of royal power.

For an American example, it is interesting to compare eighteenth century portraits of America's first president, George Washington, with those of George Hanover, the king from whom the right to govern America was fought and won. What is striking is the number of curious similarities in the way the two men are dressed and framed. A navy-blue coat, a naval hat, golden epaulets, a staff and a sword, a white powdered wig, and copious gold braid adorning their waistcoats. In the background are crowns and flags. A mace, which was the emblem of power in ancient Rome, and an eagle, a Roman symbol of military supremacy, are both incorporated into the surrounding furniture. All these motifs are vested with associations of power and authority. Only the absence of silk and ermine in the portraits of Washington make clear that in him we are not looking at a king or an emperor, but a president. Nevertheless, the similarities serve to remind us of the continuity of power. The same power has passed from one George to the other, and the vested objects in the images convey that the right to rule has passed from an old regime to a new one.

This is where we return to significance of the Ashanti Golden Throne in the story of Ghana. For the Ashanti, the most powerful people group in the country, their vested object was their Golden Throne. Like the Stone of Destiny its possession was regarded, by the Ashanti people and British colonizers alike, as something far more than symbolic. Over lunch one day at their home on the Australian east coast, my Ghanaian parents-in-law explain something of its significance to me.

"Only an anointed Ashanti King is allowed to sit upon it. For nearly fifty years the British colonizers tried to find it. They demanded that the Ashanti leaders reveal its location and allow the British Governor General to sit upon it at least once. This has never happened. Instead, the Ashanti people kept the Golden Throne hidden for half a century in a deep forest. And because no British body has ever sat upon the Golden Throne, they never

131

really had the full authority to rule in Ghana. That is why the British wanted it so badly."

I suspect this piece of history around the Ashanti vested object contributed significantly to the confidence of our Ghanaian narrator from 1948 in the previous chapter. Yet, however confident we may be, it is not easy to shake off a colonial legacy. Once the gold has been exported and used to beautify other countries' crowns and palaces, and undergird their economies and currencies; once international trading arrangements have been fixed, banking cartels and monopolies formed, commodity prices and exchange rates set, there is a great deal of invisible power that can be exerted by the former colonising country without needing to be physically present. Put simply, in any withdrawal of visible forces from a colonized country, just because the foreign position holders have been swapped for locals is not on its own a guarantee that everything has entirely changed.

However, before assessing the aftermath of the colonizer's departure, the dragon must first be faced down. That is the significance of the displays of solidarity in Ghana, beginning with the 1948 student demonstration in Cape Coast. At that point the Ghanaian movement for independence follows the classic shape of so many of the world's dragon narratives, because in almost every dragon story there comes a point where the people who have been forced to serve the dragon come together and agree that they no longer wish to live as slaves of a cold-blooded being with no love or fellow feeling for them. They will no longer accept the taxation of their resources and the conscription of their young people. They have reached the point when every draconian means of terror and control has been used long enough to have finally lost its power to persuade. The culture of subjection and depression has tipped over into grassroots anger. In this moment the people realize that if

132

they act together, and confront the dragon with one voice, saying, *"Not one of us will serve you any longer,"* what can the dragon do? *"It can't kill us all. If it did it would have no servants left, so what would be the point? It might kill a few of us, but if we stay solid, it will realize that its power to rule over us with threats of violence is at an end."*

In some versions of the story, a brave prince or hero rises up and confronts the dragon, spectacularly killing it for all to see. *Daniel in Bel and the Dragon* would be one example. George of *Saint George and the Dragon* would be another. In other stories, when the dragon sees the people standing as one and refusing to kowtow, it realises the mathematics of persecution has pivoted. Its despotic game is up, and so the dragon flees the towns and cities of the humans and retreats to the mountains to live out its life in isolation. These stories carry an obvious social message. It is a message about the power of fear to pacify and control people, the power that rises when fear is overcome, and the power of grassroots solidarity to outflank abusive patterns of leadership.

In my own lifetime I have watched this pivotal moment play out on the international stage several times over in real time. For instance, I remember the vast crowds standing in front of Ferdinand and Imelda Marcos in the Philippines in 1986. The people's refusal to accept their ongoing governance was clear. The Marcos administration's corruption, the human rights abuses, and the imprisonment and torture of tens of thousands of Filipinos had taken the people first to despair and then beyond to an angry refusal to take any more oppression from this terrible regime. By 1986, the regime had used terror to the point of terror losing its power. When the moment of confrontation came, the Marcos family could read the mood of the crowd for themselves. Their twenty-one-year long reign was at an end. Overpowered by the people's solidarity, the Marcos family had to flee, not like the proverbial dragon to the mountains, but to another country altogether.

In that same decade I can remember the dramatic scenes in Romania's Revolution Square in 1989 when President Nicolae and Elena Ceasescu failed to pacify a crowd no longer willing to live in subjection to their rule. Within twenty-four hours the Ceausescus had lost power, and within four days they were deceased. In that same year, I sat spellbound in front of my television as armed guards in Berlin stood to one side, doing absolutely nothing, as crowds of people worked together to chip away, rock from side to side and gradually pull down vast chunks of the wall which, for half a century, had divided East Berlin from West Berlin. Less than two months later, glued to the screen of of the same television I watched in awe as Nelson Mandela walked to freedom and announced a new era of democracy for South Africa. The dragon of South African Apartheid had been slain.

In the case of South African Apartheid, the African National Congress focussed the world's attention on the persecution of one individual. Thus the campaign for freedom and democracy in South Africa became the *"Free Nelson Mandela"* movement and all around the world thousands and tens of thousands stood up in solidarity to send a message to the governments of Botha and then de Klerk. And the rest is history. These were turning points in world history, reminding people everywhere that things can change for the better, and that when powerless people at the grassroots come together and act collectively, amazing things can happen. Whether the dragon is a despotic ruler, a colonising family, or a dehumanising system, the dragon can be defeated. Grassroots collaboration and solidarity really do have the power to depose the draconian regime.

The very same message is embedded in I Samuel 8's report of the great coup in which the right to govern the people of Israel passes by popular demand from YHWH to a human successor, Saul. It fits perfectly into the story arc of the world's dragon narratives as a story of social progress. Furthermore the motif of a transfer of governance from non-human entities to human beings belongs to many other indigenous narratives which tell the same story but without invoking dragon imagery. For example, the Edo people of Nigeria and Southern Benin speak of the original non-human rulers as the *Ogiso* (rulers from the sky) who hand their power over to their successors, the *Oba* – a word which simply means *leaders*. The same transition can be found in the annals of Norse and Greek legend. It is there too in the ancient Sumerian story in which Gilgamesh the hybrid king, part human and part Sky People, is the crossover king. The Hebrew narrative fits this same pattern with the appearance of Saul as the first human monarch in the story of the nation of Israel.

What does it mean to see the story of YHWH's overthrow in this wider context? Most fundamentally, it challenges the traditional reading of this chapter as a God-story. If in this episode we interpret the *Yahweh* character as a figure for *Almighty God,* then the story of his replacement by a human monarch becomes utterly absurd. Why would a society want to swap Almighty God for a human being? If the goal was to do better in diplomacy or warfare, how could a human king possibly give them a better advantage than Almighty God? However, when YHWH is understood as a non-human colonizer, the familiar arc of the dragon story comes clearly into focus. It is a lesson in social development and progress. Yahweh's dismissal reminds us that when we refuse to be cowed by the threats of harm on which so much human governance depends, when we move beyond habit and fear, when we find strength in one another and collaborate to serve the common good rather than slave for superiors, then we can create new patterns and generate positive change for our society at large. However, the moment we interpret YHWH as *God*, these empowering messages about grassroots energy and social progress instantly vanish in a puff of smoke. To understand why the original Hebrew authors wanted future generations to know about this moment in their history we have to read it in its proper context, as a story of paleocontact.

In the ages of human monarchy which follow the great coup of I Samuel 8, the Hebrew chroniclers make occasional references to various physical items, previously associated with YHWH, which have now become the vested objects of the Jewish Monarchy. Precisely what these vested objects were, how they functioned, and why they mattered are questions we will explore in the following chapter. Together we will see how the authority vested in an object may sometimes relate to the kudos or authority of a previous culture. Other times vested objects reveal themselves to be more than mere symbols of power. Sometimes they are the advanced technology of a previous civilization. If that sounds like a stretch, then turn the page and join me in in the silent streets of a forgotten city, its megalithic structures long reclaimed by the forces of nature, and now immersed in the deep, dark forests of the Yucatan peninsula.

Chapter Nine

Bloodletting, Bluetooths, and Covert Powers

Guatemala 2023

In the lush, forested area of Petén Basin, megalithic remains have been uncovered across an excavation area of more than 6,000 square miles (16,000 square kilometres.) To date, excavations have unearthed in excess of 3,000 buildings. These are the remains of the Mayan city of Tikal (*Ti-Ak'al*). From among the ruins archaeologists have retrieved fascinating artefacts of the Mayan culture which once thrived on the Yucatan peninsula. Now housed in the dark chambers of the Museum of Archaeology and Ethnology in Guatemala City, each item, safely encased in its glass enclosure and bathed in a yellow spotlight, reveals another aspect of the ceremonial and headwear of the kings and priests of Guatemala's Mayan past. One ancient carving shows a face behind a helmet with a clear visor and what looks like breathing apparatus in front of the mouth and nose. Another carved figure depicts a similar helmet as part of an entire outfit, which closely resembles a modern spacesuit. There are numbers of gold artefacts. The curators' labels tell me that these small golden items are representations of wasps. I am not so sure. The logic of their exquisite crafting, the use of as precious a material as gold, and the use of these objects as personal adornments all strongly suggest that in reality these items represented something far more valuable. For a twenty-first century viewer, it is impossible not to recognize in their design the morphology of flying craft, similar to a modern single-pilot fighter jet. On its own this collection makes Guatemala City more than worth the visit. It is a treasury of cultural memory in hard copy.

A day away from here, across the border and into what is now Mexico, lies the Mayan city of Yaxchilan. Flanking the Usamacinta River this site has been excavated to the point of identifying over one hundred structures and monuments. Among the reliefs and carvings, is a sequence of scenes carved into the limestone lintels of Yaxchilan's ancient buildings. All are deeply interesting. In particular, *Lintel 24* from *Structure 23* shows a detail of a mysterious ceremony of bloodletting. Similar to a near death ceremony, its intention was to alter the state of consciousness of the practitioner. As I peer at the ceremony I see the Mayan Queen K'ab'al Xook undertaking a fascinating ceremony. I am deeply struck by the queen's commitment to undergo what would clearly have been a painful ritual. It makes me wonder what brews the queen may have ingested to make it more bearable. Standing over Queen Xook, supervising, is her husband, King Itzaamnaj B'ahlam as he oversights the exercise of controlled blood-loss. Through the perforation and stimulation of her tongue, the Queen induces a state of delirium, and the carvings reveal a resultant alteration to her perceptual field.

The surrounding reliefs reveal that this is an exercise of remote communication between Queen Xook and a world beyond. Somehow, across the dimensions she is communicating with a powerful dragon-like being associated with her people's deep ancestry. According to Mayan ancestral story these dragon-like entities, the feathered serpents, were the beings who gave birth to the Mayan people and governed over them in the distant past. The Jaguar Dynasty, represented in these carvings by Queen Xook and King Itzaamnaj B'ahlam, understood themselves to be the rightful successors to the dragons, ruling in their stead, invoking their power and authority, and actively seeking their guidance from afar to rule over the Mayan people.

My previous travels in Africa, South America, and ancient Greece, have shown me that Queen Xook's ceremony echoes in shamanistic rituals all around the world, in which altered states of consciousness are induced as a means to achieving communication with the Powerful Ones of previous generations or of previous civilizations or of other worlds. It is especially significant that Queen Xook is pictured performing precisely this kind of contact ceremony in a city whose name Ti-Ak'al in the Yucatan Mayan language means *"The Place of the Voices."*

This informative scene is one of a number of relief carvings at Yaxcilan whose themes emit the same message. Together they serve to authenticate the intelligence, advancement and right to rule of the Mayan royal family of that time, the priestly kings of the Jaguar Dynasty. In every relief the royals are shown wearing elaborate costumes all of which include an earpiece and a mouthpiece strongly resembling what you and I would call a Bluetooth. And it is not the only apparent piece of advanced technology in evidence. Survey the hard copy of Mayan memory with a twenty-first century eye and you will be unable to miss the shapes of flying craft, space helmets, breathing apparatus, visors, aerials, and Bluetooth earpieces and microphones. If we ask why the Mayans would have depicted twenty-first century technology in carvings which are centuries old, the standard academic answer is straightforward.

"What you are looking at are the depictions of ceremonial dress used by Mayan leaders to represent their advancement and authority. This is what the priestly kings and queens wore to legitimize their dynasty. It showed their right to rule over the people and to act as judges."

Of course, this response only goes halfway to answering the question. Why were these particular symbols used? Where did the craftsmen who created these artefacts get these motifs from? What were they copying? Why would something looking like breathing apparatus or a Bluetooth become a symbol of superiority in a pre-technological world? Queen Xook is in the Place of the Voices – the very name of which implies remote communication. And a Bluetooth is a remote communication device. This is a compelling correlation. However, the bloodletting ceremony in the Place of the Voices may have something else to tell us about the anomalous earpiece. The fact that the ceremony has to drain blood in order to facilitate contact points us to two possibilities. One is that we are looking at a form of interactive technology that we don't understand, one which interfaces artificial technology with consciousness. The other possibility is that the Bluetooth in the carving was not actually functional, and that shamanic rituals have been layered over the top of technology that the Jaguar priests and royals did not know how to engineer or replicate. A real Bluetooth doesn't need an altered state of consciousness. In other words the Bluetooth of Jaguar ritual dress may have been a copy of technology which their ancestors had seen used by a previous advanced culture or civilization. If we cross-refer Mayan archaeological finds with the artefacts of Mayan literature, then the evidence points us in this second direction.

Mayan texts speak of powerful beings, the draconian feathered serpents, who colonized and adapted the ancestors of the Mayan people. They first appeared, hovering over the primordial waters, in advanced flying craft. According to the story, they did indeed have advanced technology. The Mayan narrative of the Popol Vuh goes on to detail the textures of the advanced craft and how they appeared when in action in the night sky. If we consider these text as cultural memory then the emblems we find in Guatemala and

Mexico could very well be hard copy records of those ancient visitors, evoking the things they wore and the technology they brought with them. If I am right about that, then it makes perfect sense that these motifs would be invoked in the ceremonial dress of the human kings and queens who succeeded the dragons as governing powers. To wear these emblems was essentially a claim to be the rightful successors of the Powerful Ones of the past, and the legitimate inheritors of their authority. Put simply, the motifs of ancient technology were the vested objects of the Mayan culture.

In a few paragraphs we will take a moment to look at the ancient Hebrew equivalents of the Mayan helmets, Bluetooth earpieces and microphones. We will find them embedded in the cultic practice of C11th-10thBCE Judaism. But first I want to point out the rationale of this kind of claim to ultimate authority. The monarchs of the Jaguar Dynasty emphasised in their lore and ritual that their power and right to rule were derived from an earlier regime, a prior culture, a previous civilization and ultimately from outer space. This logic is applied even in the twenty-first century. The Scottish Stone of Destiny legitimizes Charles III's reign over Scotland because it embodies a continuity of use going back to previous kings, and previous cultures, going back in time through England, Scotland, Ireland, Greece, Spain, Egypt, Syria, the Levant and ultimately, via the standing stones of Bethel to outer space. From C8thCE Mexico to C21stCE Britain. the same ET root to royal power is implied. This claim is no different to that of the ancient Sumerian kings who claimed an unbroken succession from the ET Sky People, as detailed on the Sumerian Kings' List, now housed in Britain's Ashmolean Museum. It is no different to the people of Benin claiming their traditional leaders, the Oba, as successors from the ET Ogiso leaders from the sky. Coincidence?

141

We might attempt to explain this pattern away in more prosaic terms. A sceptic might say that this is simply about how contemporary leaders want others to see them, framing themselves as *"worthy successors to King or Queen So-and-So the Great"*. However there may be another layer to peel back. Why would a powerful sovereign like Itzaamnaj B'ahlam or K'ab'al Xook need the guidance and say-so from a non-human ruler who had already had their go on the throne? Precisely the same question could be put to the successors of YHWH in the Hebrew chronicles because, after all the effort of organising the tribes and tribal leaders of Israel to stage their coup and depose king YHWH, there is something out of order about the persistence of YHWH's role in Israel's political life. Is that really what the people had in mind when they gave him his marching orders?

What this part of the YHWH narrative reveals relates not only to the behaviour of past cultures or the possibility of previous civilizations. It informs how we understand the workings of power in the political world of today. The odd post-script to the great coup of I Samuel 8 is that despite his removal from the political front bench, YHWH's ability to influence the exercise of crown power over Israel is far from over. As subsequent dramas play out it becomes clear that the deposed elohim has simply become a backseat driver. Indeed he does everything he can to undermine his immediate successor's exercise of power. For instance, though Saul is the king on the throne, YHWH still expects to drive Israel's foreign policy. Of course, a country cannot have two foreign policies. One or other must prevail. So where did that leave King Saul?

The inevitable crunch point for King Saul occurs when he fails to enact Yahweh's preferred policy of scorched Earth in a war of

Yahweh's engineering. On this infamous occasion, King Saul misunderstood YHWH's wishes, and having won the battle decisively, he brings YHWH a generous tribute of all his favourite things, gold, beef, lamb, and virgin girls, which Saul expects to leave in YHWH's Temple for the next time the mysterious Powerful One should happen to show up. However, YHWH's deputy, the king-maker Samuel, tells Saul that because he neglected to have his troops slaughter every man, woman, child, and every living thing, YHWH will not accept his offerings. Instead he will see to it that Saul's reign was now finished.

However, so the story goes, YHWH does far more than simply withdraw his approval from his human successor, infesting Saul's body with a mysterious parasitic life-form to make the king mentally ill, and torment and diminish Saul's life to the point at which, in a state of mental anguish, and still desperate to please his powerful predecessor, Saul takes his own life. And this is how YHWH treats his friends! King Saul never saw himself as an enemy of YHWH. He clearly regarded himself as YHWH's vice regent and made clear in many ways that his intention was only ever to honour his powerful predecessor and overlord. Even before Saul is finally dead YHWH's deputy selects and swears in, Saul's successor, David, to be a worthy king in the tradition of YHWH.

Consider the drama of that episode for a moment. Does it seem odd that the rejected, non-human king Yahweh is still muscling in on the affairs of government, giving his approval or disapproval, issuing death warrants, and dismissing and anointing kings? After all, it is not as if the people had moved him from being Prime-Minister to President. They had wanted him replaced and out of the picture. But, if YHWH's ongoing involvement seems baffling or out of order, then allow me to show you that in reality it is part of a wider and longer pattern of political successions. What we see playing out in the politics of C11th-C8thBCE Judaism can be seen in the history of more than one modern nation, but I will share with you the parallel that I know best, that of the country of my birth, Great Britain. In the next couple of pages let me unpack how the continuity of old powers has manifested in Britain and as I do you will recognize that YHWH's persistent, covert presence is part of a widespread and deeply embedded pattern in the ways of the world.

Great Britain 2023

Once upon a time, Britain was a collection of monarchies. Gradually it evolved into a single monarchy, governed by a single king. In 1215 the powers of the Crown were limited by the Magna Carta. This was the collaborative work of the country's senior barons who, having joined together in solidarity, gathered around the king to curtail his powers and show him how things were now going to work, moving forward. Four and a half centuries later the Westminster parliament went even further and abolished the office of king altogether, and in 1649 executed the incumbent monarch, King Charles I, to emphasize the point.

After eleven years as a republic, parliament appointed a new monarch in 1660, King Charles II, albeit with firmer boundaries around his kingly powers. In 1688 the Glorious Revolution then moved the power to govern from the Crown to Parliament. Since that time the power to legislate has been extended to the democratically elected House of Commons, albeit checked by the House of Lords, a body of legislators appointed by the Crown. Later, the social reforms of the 1800s extended the voting franchise to include all adult males, and the reforms of the 1900s extended the voting franchise to all adult females. The labour movement of the 1900s created new generations of leaders willing to represent the interests of working Britons, firstly in the workplace and then in parliament, with the purpose of achieving policies which would serve the interests of ordinary Britons, and not just the one percent.

Given the seismic scale of these shifts towards democracy over the span of eight centuries you may be surprised at the continuity of non-democratic monarchical power. For instance, despite eight hundred years of rebellions, coups, revolutions, and democratic reforms, in twenty-first century Britain, a democratically elected Prime Minister, in order to be allowed to serve, must first receive an invitation to the palace, for him or her to kneel in front of the King or Queen, kiss the sovereign's hand, swear their oath of office as well as an oath of allegiance to the King or Queen. This is called *"swearing in."* The person being bowed to, kissed, and sworn fealty to will be the senior British member of the extended dynastic family of John William Friso, the Saxe-Coburg-Gotha Family. If those names are unfamiliar to you it is because in 1917, to make themselves sound less like German colonizers, and more like an English family, the Saxe-Coburg-Gotha family decided to rename themselves after an English royal town, and so they became referred to instead as *"The Windsors."* Although democratically elected, the British Prime Minister is still required to obtain permission to form a government from the reigning Windsor, and then for the entirety of their tenure, is required to report to the reigning Windsor once a week every week in order to account for their political activity. Furthermore, any and every piece of legislation passed by the parliament has to be signed off by his or her majesty before it can become law.

Even after eight centuries of democratisation in Britain, of the 1,418 parliamentarians serving today, fewer than half are democratically elected, only 46%. The majority of Britain's parliamentarians, 54% to be precise, are either distant relatives of the Windsor Family or are given their seats in parliament by the reigning Windsor on the advice of the Prime Minister. Furthermore, every member of parliament, once elected, is required to swear an oath of allegiance to the reigning member of the Windsor family before being allowed even to sit in Parliament. Technically no republican can ever hold office as a member of parliament in Great Britain, even if democratically elected, simply because it would be contrary to the solemn oath of allegiance to the Windsor family.

Other significant powers still reside with the Windsor family. These include the power to appoint ministers, to police the public, to exclude the police from Windsor family properties, the power to deprive members of the public of their liberty, to issue death warrants, embargo state information, negate criminal liability, defend borders, go to war, and raise and spend taxes. Some of these crown powers are delegated or loaned to the Prime Minister, others are delegated to Police and Intelligence services, and some are exercised directly. But they are all *"Crown Powers"* and as such they fall outside of any democratic control or accountability.

In my own lifetime, these powers have been used directly by the Crown to amend some legislation, and in other cases exempt the Crown from new legislation. For instance, in 1968, as a move towards negating endemic racism in the country, the British Labour government under Prime Minister Harold Wilson, brought forward a bill to make it illegal to refuse a person employment on the basis of their ethnicity. The white paper was brought to parliament, read in the House of Commons and House of Lords and finally passed into law, but only after Queen Elizabeth II had demanded an exemption from this law for all palaces, properties and estates owned by her family. In those places all the *"old ways"* would continue unabated, thank you very much! And this exemption was far from a one-off. In fact, in the last fifty-five years of her reign, the late Queen Elizabeth II obtained similar exemptions for her family from one hundred and sixty pieces of legislation. These exemptions included laws governing animal welfare and workers' rights. In my lifetime, crown powers have been used to refuse police access, avoid legal scrutiny, shut down successive police investigations into elite crime, and to depose a democratically elected prime-minister on the other side of the world in the Windsors' dominion of Australia.

As a citizen of Australia I have learned that the situation in Britain's dominions is even more interesting. In Australia, for instance, we like to think we own the houses and land that we pay for. However, the uncomfortable truth is that whenever you *"purchase"* a property in Australia, your conveyancer, if they are doing their job, will point in the terms of your contract to a prior claim on your property. It is the claim of ownership by the Windsor family. Technically, all an Australian can ever do is buy a lease on land already owned by the Windsor family. And when we die, through a subtle cocktail of taxes, a percentage of the equity we may have built up through our lives' work will be taken and given to enrich the dominion's national coffer. By total contrast if a person dies while in possession of Britain's vested objects, the crown, the orb, the sceptre, the jewels and the rest, the wealth of that person will not be taxed. Their family can keep the money, so that the wealth of the Windsor family is never dispersed in the way yours and mine is.

By now I have probably made the point. These crown powers are far from ceremonial. They represent a hidden hand in the political operations of what looks on the surface like a democracy. The fact that the crown jewels are still the *"crown jewels"* and not *"the nation's jewels"* or *"parliament's jewels"* or *"the prime-minister's jewels"* turns out to matter. Minus the gracious loan of the Stone of Destiny back to Scotland, when not being used to crown English kings and queens in Westminster, these time-honoured vested objects remain crown possessions, perpetually anchoring the Windsor family's right to reign. Perhaps this really does matter. And perhaps it connects with the persistence of unaccountable crown powers after eight centuries of attempting democratic reform.

In the light of my humble sketch of the persistence of old powers in Great Britain, you will now see the parallels with YHWH's *"removed but not removed"* or *"retired but not retired"* status in the affairs of the rulers of Israel. It is the exact same dynamic which plays out in the stories of Yahweh, Saul, David, and their entire line of successors. Think again about the apparent need for YHWH, the rejected ruler, to approve the anointing of Saul and David as kings. How is that? As Israel's rejected sovereign, by what right did he then remove his successor Saul? Also, by what right does it remain YHWH's right to receive revenue from Israel's acquisitions of neighbouring territory? Whether YHWH has retained these powers through the possession of vested objects, or simply by having superior firepower, is a theme only hinted at in the Hebrew Scriptures. But when seen alongside the story of British crown power, YHWH's apparent retirement from visible leadership to a place of power behind the throne could be viewed as a kind of template, a way to create an illusion of change and social progress, in which the visible leader or even government systems change, while the unaccountable powers shaping public policy behind the scenes remain totally unaltered. Today we have a name for this kind of hidden power. We call it *"covert government."*

148

In Australia, where I live, in Britain where I grew up, in the U.SA. and other countries besides, it is not uncommon for major corporations to make significant financial donations to both of the major parties in a general election so that whichever party gains power there will be kickbacks and the same corporate power will be rewarded with influence in the shaping of public policy. In that sense money itself, and access to large sums of it, could be regarded as the vested object of modern political life. All the while the visible, elected leaders can be swapped and changed while the covert engines of policy remain unchanged and unaccountable. The stories of the kings in the Hebrew Scriptures speak with the same insight when read through the lens of paleocontact and colonization.

As to the vested objects named in the Biblical narratives, the Hebrew equivalent of the Scottish Stone of Destiny, or the Mayan Bluetooth, or the Ashanti Golden Throne is a sacred item known as the *Ark of the Covenant*. It represented the right to govern the tribes of Israel, and the power to obtain guidance from on high. Without ever explaining how, the Biblical narrator indicates that the function of the Ark was to facilitate remote communication between the king, seated adjacent to the Ark, and the powerful YHWH, who mysteriously was otherwise inaccessible. In Exodus 25:22 YHWH tells Moses that when he is *in cathedra*, meaning when Moses is enthroned adjacent to the Ark, *"I [YHWH] will meet with you and give you all my commands for the Israelites."* Rather like the Pope when he is seated *"in cathedra,"* so Moses' words spoken when he is seated by the Ark will carry the full authority of YHWH and must therefore be believed and obeyed absolutely.

In essence, therefore, the Ark of the Covenant was both the throne of power and a communications device. The Hebrew people's other vested objects were stored within the Ark of the Covenant to add to its kudos. These included the staff of Aaron (the spokesperson for Moses.) It too represented power and authority from YHWH. (This is mentioned in Numbers 17.) A third vested object stored within the Ark was a jar of manna, the mysterious substance provided by YHWH in the desert, another embodiment of YHWH's supernatural power. Exodus 16 names a fourth set of vested objects, the tablets of The Law given by YHWH, embodying his sovereign will and symbolising the authority to govern and legislate in his name. But what exactly was the Ark? Its function is described, and its design is prescribed in great detail in its story of origin in Exodus 25. But how did it work? Was it merely a totem, or part of the paraphernalia of a shamanic ritual with other esoteric layers, like those of the Mayan bloodletting ceremony? Or was the Ark a communications device of a more technological kind? A number of strange phenomena surrounding the history of the Ark suggest this last explanation may be the correct one.

For instance, in one place the Biblical narrator shows the Ark being used to create powerful vortices of wind, and on others it emits what to a modern eye looks like electricity and radiation. On one occasion, a rival people group captures the Ark in a battle. This is recorded in I Samuel 4. Having brought it back into their community they proudly install it in the temple of their Powerful One, Dagon. The neighbours in question, the Philistines, are thrilled because they assume they have taken possession of an object vested with imperial power. However, the narrator of I Samuel 4 reports with some delight that the Philistines' own vested object, a statue of their powerful one, Dagon, promptly falls down when in the presence of the Hebrew Golden Throne. This happens two days running, and on the second occasion the image of Dagon breaks into pieces..

In this detail the narrator reveals his clear conviction that YHWH is superior to Dagon. Represented respectively by the Ark and the statue, Dagon in effect bows down to YHWH on day one, and is destroyed by YHWH on day two. Dagon was the Philistine's name for a powerful one from the past, who like the Babylonian Oannes, was semiaquatic. Like Oannes in Babylon, and Asherah in Judaism, the Philistines remembered Dagon for having appeared in the deep past to teach their ancestors all the secrets of agricultural science and city-building. In other words, Dagon embodied the Philistine story of paleocontact. It is a tradition the YHWHistic narrator takes delight in mocking through the drama of the Ark and the statue.

Unfortunately the story of the Philistines' woes does not end there. In the days following their capture of the Ark, the Philistines' territory becomes overrun with rats and the population breaks out in tumours. Their misfortunes continue until, finally, they decide to place YHWH's vested objects on the back of a cart drawn by two oxen and ship them back post haste to their original owners. Whatever the precise nature of the underlying events, the story reveals the YHWHistic narrator's disdain for the other powerful ones and his high esteem of the Hebrew vested objects.

Two other vested objects housed within the Ark were the *Urim* and the *Thummim*. Like the Ark of the Covenant itself, these mysterious items embodied an esoteric technology by which ancient Jewish leaders would expect to communicate with YHWH and receive information and guidance from the great unknown. Some scholars suggest that the heady cocktail of smokes and oils saturating the air of the inner sanctuary were intended to assist the priests' interaction with the other side by effecting an altered state of consciousness. Yet the Bible's vague language surrounding the purpose of the oils and smokes, and especially around the urim and thummim strongly suggests that neither their priestly users nor the later narrators had any real idea what the objects actually were or how they really functioned. This not knowing strongly suggests two possibilities concerning this mysterious technology. The first is that what the high priests were actually handling was in fact the advanced technology of a previous or extra-terrestrial civilization. The second is that, like Queen Xook's earpiece, the urim and thummim were artistic low-tech facsimiles of an advanced communications technology which their ancestors had seen operated in the past by a previous culture or by the Powerful Ones themselves.

The parallels with the activity of the shamanic Queen Xook in ancient Guatemala are really quite striking. Both cultures saw the right to rule as coming to them from the past, with roots in an extra-terrestrial narrative, and with the transfer of power represented by vested objects. Equally significant is that both the priestly kings and queens of the Jaguar Dynasty and the kings and high priests of ancient Judaism expected to exercise their rule on behalf of beings associated with dragons. And both royal priestly lines expected to effect remote communication with their respective dragon-entities through a combination of altered states and esoteric technology. Just like the spectacular Mayan raiment of extra-terrestrial technology, so the vested objects of Judaism bore the symbology of power without their human owners ever knowing how the items portrayed really worked.

Whatever the mystery surrounding the vested objects within Judaism, their political signifiance is clear. The Jewish kings and high priests were merely human position-holders or proxies for YHWH. Regardless of YHWH's departure from the front bench, the cult of YHWH would still define what was or was not

152

acceptable public policy and if things strayed too far in another direction, then there would be consequences. Punitive action would follow and the hidden hand of YHWH would find one way or another to hoik things back to where he would prefer. The stories of Yahweh, Saul, and David and the kings and prophets who follow them serve as an object lesson in the *realpolitik* of leadership succession. They dramatize the critical insight that just because a society has replaced a dragon with a human, or an old king with a new king, or has deposed a king and appointed a prime-minister, or has defeated a foreign colonial power and installed its own president, none of these changes guarantees that the former power has actually relinquished its influence. The former despot may still be in possession of the vested objects, such as the monarchs of Great Britain with their sceptre, orb, the Stone of Destiny, and the rights to other people's land and properties in distant dominions. The former ruler may continue to pull significant strings from behind closed doors, just as Yahweh did with Saul, David and their successors. Resources may continue to trickle up from the general population, and into the coffers of the old rulers, whether by way of tithes, tax, banking systems or trade arrangements or, as in the case of YHWH, directly through patterns of tribute. In ways like this, all the dynamics of government established by the old regime are able to persist under the appearance of a new leader.

Our ancestors were wise to all these patterns. They understood the modalities of colonization, and unaccountable power, and were able to perceive the dynamics of abusive leadership. They had a knowledge of vested objects, the principles of covert government, and were well aware of hidden hands in geopolitics, and the non-human layer to human governance. They then wove these vital insights into their stories and sagas, to serve as a political education for future generations, in the hope that their descendants would be spared the ignorance and suffering of their forefathers.

The great tragedy is that this ancestral wisdom has been redacted and translated out of existence, so that you and I are now left scratching the ground for signs of the treasure they buried, gradually piecing together what it was they wanted us to know. All the socio-political lessons I have outlined in the last couple of chapters depend on reading the Bible's narratives from the perspective of paleocontact. This perspective completely evaporates the instant we translate YHWH as God. When we read about the great coup in I Samuel 8 through the dragon-story lens, then the moment when the people discover their collective power and face the monster down is a moment to be met by the hearers of the story with cheers and congratulations. It is a high moment, a moment of celebration with empowering implications as we contemplate today's political realities. By contrast, if we imagine YHWH to be God and read the episode through the lens of God-story, then replacing YHWH with a human king can only be seen as a moment of idiocy, rebellion, and apostasy, and the lesson in civics appears to be nothing more than, *"Put up and shut up!"* The opposite of grassroots power.

More than any moment in the Biblical story, the dismissal of YHWH puts the C6thBCE redactor in an awkward position. The redactor's remit is essentially to demonstrate the YHWHistic *bona fides* of the Jewish kings. Yet the founding moment of the Jewish monarchy is a moment wherein the rule of YHWH is being rejected. This is a Catch 22 for sure. On the one hand, if the redactor celebrates the foundation of the Jewish monarchy too enthusiastically then he risks casting YHWH in a bad light. On the other hand, if he sides unequivocally with YHWH he risks making the very foundation of the Jewish monarchy appear

154

ungodly or anti-YHWH, which is the very opposite of his editorial agenda. To avoid either error, the redactor has to walk a fine line. The approach he adopts in this instance is essentially the same as the redactor's general approach, which studiedly makes *"no moral comment wherever the actions of YHWH are concerned."*

For the three millennia since, the implication of this editorial decision has been, *"God is not to be questioned."* This is the foundational decision which established from that time to this that *"God"* is permitted to do, in the words of Origen, *"such things as we would not believe of the most savage and unjust of men,"* without us even flinching or considering for an instant that he has done anything wrong. However, if we choose to accept this editorial gloss, then we have essentially surrendered our own mind and our own conscience. Today readers can make up their own minds. Judge for yourself, is the extreme violence of the character YHWH the holy activity of a divine, transcendent being? Or is it the brutalism of a psychopathic colonizer?

This is a question I am going to put, only more politely than that, to a pastor friend of mine, later this evening. I am staying at his place in California on my way to a conference. The pastor in question is not Lance! No. Lance loves to preach the violence of Yahweh from the pulpit. Lance is one of those fiery preachers, and I know I am not going to get him across the line. No, my host for this evening is the charismatic pastor of a mega-church in the U.S. whose own paranormal experiences have convinced him that humanity enjoys a good deal more company in the cosmos than the theology of his youth ever permitted him to believe. He has been working on the question of how to hold his faith and his paranormal experiences together in a way that makes sense. But what is really eating at him right now is an even knottier question.

What will happen when he shares these conclusions with his congregation?

Chapter Ten

Enter the Destroyer

Santa Barbara, California – January 2023

"Paul, I am almost entirely with you. I agree with perhaps ninety percent of what you're saying. My problem is that in my denomination if you are seen to question the Bible you are viewed as challenging God, because the Bible is thought of as 'God's book.' How can I even begin to hint that the Bible was originally about something else? Politics? Paleocontact? Dragons? These are all impossible. I can't see my people accepting any of those ideas as Biblical agendas. And if I lose my teaching relationship with my people by busting their bubble, then I can't teach them anything. So, I really have to think very carefully about what to do with all this."

I completely sympathise. Cary is the pastor of a congregation in a well-known charismatic denomination in the U.S.A. People's association in the churches of that denomination is based on a shared set of beliefs and practices, some official and some unofficial. So the very foundation of those groups creates an environment in which pastors have to respect a lot of doctrinal boundaries. There are a lot of theological *"No Entry"* signs restricting where their thinking is allowed to take them. In many churches of this kind, junior pastors arriving fresh from seminary, freshly educated to the level of a bachelor's degree, will quickly learn to bite their lip. The signals will be everywhere that if they were to share what they have learned at theological college – especially about the Bible – they would run the risk of immediately losing their job. It's not about who has done the study and who hasn't. Whether you are *"in"* or *"out"* is defined purely by a willingness to repeat the doctrinal norms of that group

This isn't Cary's situation, however. He is a very well-respected senior pastor and his current tenure is far from his first rodeo. In fact, Cary is the CEO of what in Australia we would consider to be a *"megachurch."* The reason Cary needs to think carefully and go gently is simply that he takes very seriously his responsibility to teach and to lead the people entrusted to him. If he were simply to download all his current conclusions and speculations, it might bring a certain sense of relief to him personally, he would be out-of-the-closet but it would, as he rightly points out, effectively end his teaching relationship with his people. For that reason, I completely respect the pace at which Cary is exploring this territory, and the pace at which he is choosing to share the what he finds along the way.

"Cary, I think the start point for a lot of people in your denomination is that they love how Jesus presents the idea of God. Any of them who have read the Bible will have noticed that the behaviour of the God-character in the Old Testament is incompatible with the morality taught by Jesus. So they are halfway to recognising that the old stories must be about something else."

"How about, whenever these dissonant moments occur in the scriptures, you leave them unresolved? How about you state the questions and leave them hanging? Give people permission to see what they are seeing and feel what they are feeling. If you take away the pressure to have everything locked down, if you show people the questions, I think the Bible is enough on its own to unravel all our old assumptions about what those stories are really about. Could you approach it that way?"

I hope I am right about the texts being enough on their own when given sufficient attention, because the persistence of old paradigms is something to be wondered at. Both Cary, from his vantage at the pulpit, and I from my vantage in front of the camera, wonder how long it will be before we reach a tipping point where all the pastors and theologians who, behind closed doors, know that the Bible's Yahweh and elohim stories were not originally God-stories, feel able to come forward and say so? When that moment comes then we can all ask together the obvious next question, *"What did our ancestors wish to teach us through their descriptions of ancient contact and colonization?"* Presumably they wanted to equip us to avoid the pain of the past and chart a better future. The stories we have touched on in the last couple of chapters hint at powerful psychological and socio-political lessons which we might have applied more confidently and more universally for more than two millennia, if only the redactors translators hadn't obscured those lessons and hidden them from us.

My al fresco dinner with Cary is progressing very slowly with whole paragraphs of crossfire conversation between each mouthful, but I feel Cary and I are making good progress as we compare notes and work out where we can find a common understanding. It is so refreshing to have a conversation where it is alright to be explorative and where neither of us feels we have to be on guard or defensive. Though we each would struggle to cross each other's i's and dot each other's t's we both respect each other as seekers of truth and understanding. By the time the evening cools and we segue inside for coffee, Cary is hitting a run of $64,000 questions.

"So, Paul, if the elohim stories are not about God, if they really are about paleocontact, and if the Yahweh stories are the retelling of stories about past colonization by non-human beings, does Almighty God even show up in the Bible?"

"I mean, in my denomination we don't recite creeds as part of our worship, but of course we are aware of them, and we recognize them as definitive statements of faith. The creed says, 'We believe in God, the Father, the Almighty.' Once we have deconstructed all the root meanings of all the names we thought were God, does the Almighty God of the creeds actually show up in the Bible?"

This is a question I am asked every week by people who have found me on *The 5th Kind* or the *Paul Wallis* channel, who have watched my series with Mauro Biglino or read my previous Eden books. Some weeks it's every day that I find myself in correspondence with a reader or viewer who has made the effort to contact me in person so that they can nut this matter out.

"Cary, where I am at right now, I would suggest that every time we see Yahweh as a being, physically present as an active player in the life of ancient Israel, I believe we are being presented with recollections of a physical entity. Not God. A biological entity."

"However, that's not the end of the story. The later redactors did associate the name Yahweh with an idea of God as the originator of creation. When we find the name Yahweh as an object of worship or praise, such as in the minor prophets, then I think we are looking at a concept of God similar to the vision of "The Father in the heavens" as described by Jesus, or similar to the language of the Apostle Paul when he described God as, 'The Source of the Cosmos and everything in it, that in which we all live and move and have our being, of whom we are all offspring.'

160

(That's my one sentence summary of Paul's message in Athens in Acts 17.)

"Note, though, that the Apostle Paul's cosmic explanation of God as Source is different to the image of 'Almighty God' which Jewish and Christian believers have run with for the past couple of thousand years. In fact, I would suggest that 'The Almighty' is an idea that is absent from the Bible as a whole. After all, in the Hebrew, the Bible doesn't even have a word for that concept."

Cary's raised eyebrows and pause between breaths indicates that I have caught my pastor friend by surprise. *"Wow Paul, I am not sure I can go there with you, because I would lose count of all the references to the Almighty, God Almighty, the Lord Almighty in my Bible. Every time I read those words, it hammers home the idea that there really is an Ultimate Being. There really is an Almighty God."*

Cary is certainly right about that. The peppering of *"God Almighty"* through our Bible translations really does hammer home the idea of an Almighty Ultimate Being, the Most Powerful player in the Universe. Of course, this is a conception of God which has thrown up huge problems for believers from age to age, because if God is an almighty being, then why doesn't he simply fix all the problems? If Almighty God is able to do anything he desires, then why doesn't he divinely magic everything better when that's what's needed? When we survey the horrors of human life at its darkest and most depressing, we have to ask, what kind of all-powerful entity would stand by and let things happen which are too horrendous to even speak about, let alone for people to experience? It is the question of suffering with which believers have wrestled all through the ages. These questions are inescapably thrown up by this idea of God as an almighty being.

"Cary, for me it always comes down to 'What do the words mean?!' Where you read the word 'almighty' in your Bible translation the chances are you are looking at a rendering of the name 'El Shaddai.' I would humbly suggest 'The Almighty' is a total, I might almost say 'deliberate' mistranslation of that name."

Here you might think I am really sticking my neck out a degree too far, because most English language Bibles really are peppered with references to the *Lord Almighty* or to the *Almighty*. However, I have come to the conclusion that this is a translation which deserves wholesale rejection. For support I turn to the *Brown, Driver Briggs Hebrew-English Lexicon*, which is one of the most authoritative and widely recognized dictionaries of Hebrew meanings. Of *El Shaddai* it says that as a divine name its meaning is *"still uncertain."* Given what else the dictionary has to say about that word, this may be a political answer. But I will come to that a little later.

The *New Jerusalem Bible*, whose translation and footnotes were oversighted by my monastic friend Dom Henry Wansbrough, also addresses this issue of false translation. I will always be very grateful to Dom Henry for his personal assistance when I was doing the research for my book *Escaping from Eden*. For the sake of accuracy, I am not implying that Dom Henry necessarily agrees with my conclusions. Just that he was very helpful in pointing out some of the journeys that various ancient Hebrew words may have made through time and what the original meanings may have been. I take my hat off to the *New Jerusalem Bible*. It doesn't go as far as the *Edizioni San Paulo*, leaving *elohim, elyon, el shaddai*

162

and *YHWH* untranslated, but I love the transparency with which its footnotes and editorial comments highlight some of the translation issues surrounding the names for God.

If we go to the first appearance of El Shaddai in Genesis 17 this is what the footnotes of the *New Jerusalem Bible* have to say:

"El Shaddai - an ancient divine name of the patriarchal period, rarely used outside the Pentateuch. [It is] preserved mainly in the priestly tradition...The usual translation 'Almighty God' is inaccurate..."

So, you see I am not sticking my neck out quite as far as you may have thought.

"The usual translation 'Almighty God' is inaccurate. The meaning is uncertain. 'God of the mountain' from the Akkadian 'shadu' has been suggested... Perhaps 'God of the open wastes 'would be preferable, from the Hebrew 'sade.' It is [also] the secondary meaning of the Akkadian word. It seems to have been a divine name brought from upper Mesopotamia by the ancestors of the race."

The editors of the *New Jerusalem Bible* are affirming that this name *El Shaddai* suggests a Powerful One with a regional jurisdiction, a Powerful One of the mountains or a Powerful One of the planes, or the open wastes. For a clue, a great place to begin is the moment when the *El Shaddai* figure makes his first appearance in Genesis 17.

"When Abraham was 99 years old, Yahweh appeared to Abraham and said, 'I am El Shaddai. Walk before my face, in front of me

163

and be blameless. I will make my covenant between me and you and will multiply you exceedingly."

Here the narrator equates Yahweh with El Shaddai. Indeed, this is another moment when the activity of the redactor comes into the light. A writer from after the time of Moses, who knew the name Yahweh, is retelling the story of Abraham, using the name that was later revealed. He is doing this so that the reader will understand Yahweh to have been involved in the Hebrew story from the very beginning. This same point is made emphatically in Exodus 6:3, where the text says this: *"The Powerful One spoke to Moses and said to him, 'I am Yahweh. To Abraham Isaac and Jacob, I appeared as El Shaddai, but I did not make my name Yahweh known to them."*

Here the redactor is doing everything he can to explain why the post-Moses name is appearing in the pre-Moses text. He is saying that these two names represent the same Powerful One. This then speaks to the possible meanings of the earlier name. The *New Jerusalem Bible* suggests that we are being told about a regional power, a Powerful One with a geographical jurisdiction. Indeed, the Powerful Ones of the Biblical narratives are often associated with geographical jurisdictions. For instance we hear about Akhekh the Powerful One of Egypt. There is the El of the Amorites, and the elohim of your ancestors when they lived in Mesopotamia. These are referenced in Joshua's *"Whom shall you serve"* speech in Joshua 24. We have the El of Ekron in the book of II Kings. Similarly, there is a moment in the book of Daniel when a mysterious messenger appears up in Daniel's apartment and tells him, *"I had a terrible time getting here because I had to go into battle with the Powerful One of Persia."*

Each of these powerful ones is associated with their own geographical area and it is understood that the powerful one who owns land also owns the human beings who live on it. This is an interesting idea because it is a polity which has been repeated around the world and throughout human history, the idea that if you own the land, if you are the King, or the Lord, or the Squire, then you own the people who live on that land. You can raise taxes from them, charge them rents, receive their tithes, deploy them in your armies, deprive them of liberty or execute them through your courts. This philosophy survived into the Middle Ages in Europe. It persisted in the polity of British, Spanish, French and Dutch Empires, and still survives to this day. The philosophy has its roots in the mentality of non-human governance over our ancestors. We have already seen that the Bible before God speaks of the era when elohim governed over project Earth, each receiving their respective lands and people from the hands of El Elyon. In that ancient context the geographical interpretation of *El Shaddai* as the powerful one either of the mountains or the plains, makes perfect sense. But which is it, mountains or plains?

Curiously this exact question played a critical part in a famous clash between the people of El Shaddai and their rivals the Syrians. I Kings 20:23 tells us:

"The servants of the King of Syria told him 'Yahweh, their powerful one is a powerful one of the hills or the mountains. This is why they were stronger than us..."

The Syrian strategists are saying this to explain how come their forces had just lost to the people of Israel in the mountains.

"...This is why they were stronger than us. However, if we fight them in the plain surely not! Surely, we will be stronger than them!"

Evidently, the Syrians understood the name of El Shaddai to indicate that he was a powerful one of the mountains. This would seem a pretty compelling piece of evidence if we wanted to know what the name meant in an earlier age. However, is it possible that the Syrians may have got their interpretation wrong? The way the story plays out from that moment on, the punchline of the story may well be that the Syrians had actually misinterpreted the name, and to their great cost.

This is how the story continues: El Shaddai takes great offence when he hears of the Syrian advisors' assessment. *"Oh they think I can't beat them in the plain eh! I'll show them!!"* To make things clear Yahweh then slaughters the Syrians in the battle that ensues, costing the Syrian forces 100,000 infantry in a single day of battle and a further 27,000 in a post-battle accident. Whether in the mountains or the plains didn't matter. El Shaddai was an absolute destroyer on the battlefield. And that, as it happens, is the other possible meaning of the name *El Shaddai*.

A little earlier I suggested that the authoritative *Brown, Driver Briggs Hebrew-English Lexicon* may have offered a polite or political answer when it said that *El Shaddai* as *The Almighty* was an *"uncertain"* translation. Now let me tell you why I said that. The very same lexicon argues that the root of *Shaddai* is the verb *shadad*. It means *"to act with violence, to ruin or devastate."* The obvious implication is that the name El Shaddai has nothing to do with a limitation of powers to either mountains or plains. Tellingly, in I Kings 20 El Shaddai is eager to prove this exact point. The implication of *shadad* as the root of *Shaddai* is that *El*

Shaddai then becomes *The Powerful One, the Destroyer.* This is the point he proves on the battlefield with the Syrians on that day in I Kings 20. Indeed, when you think about the genocides, infanticides, scorched earth massacres and fiery devastations, both threatened and caused by the Yahweh character in the Bible, then for his other name to mean *The Powerful One the Destroyer* would be a perfect fit.

This reading casts a revealing light on El Shaddai's very first appearance to the patriarch Abraham in Genesis 17 when he says: *"Walk before my face, Abram. Walk in front of me and be blameless."* Who is blaming? Nobody even mentioned blame! What El Shaddai is saying amounts to, *"Walk in front of me and don't do anything wrong in my sight. Walk in front of me and don't put a foot wrong."* When you imagine that this instruction has been issued by a powerful being who has just introduced himself as *"The Powerful One, The Destroyer,"* you can imagine that Abraham would be eager to please. Indeed, within two chapters, *The Powerful One, the Destroyer* has incinerated two entire cities. Could it be that the deeply embedded religious idea that Almighty God requires perfection of us, with fiery destruction on the agenda should we fail, is an idea whose roots lie here in El Shaddai's relationship with Abraham?

El Shaddai's self-introduction to Abraham accurately reflects the dynamic of a colonizer introducing himself to the newly colonized. It is the same psychopathic dual message that we saw in a previous chapter. It says, *"With one hand I will protect you and with the other I will punish you. No one will benefit you as much as I can, as long as you please me. On the other hand nobody can protect you from me if you displease me."* From the get-go, Abraham understands both the dark and the light of a being who, on the one hand promises progeny and prosperity,

167

while on the other hand demands unfailing obedience from his own people and nukes the cities of others.

This dark shadow has figured in our concepts of God ever since that fateful day in the C6thBCE when the redactors and Biblical translators began casting El Shaddai as *"The Almighty."* This false equation has distorted our concept of God and of our place in the cosmos from that day to this. *Elohim, elyon, Yahweh* and *El Shaddai* are all words which have long been understood as names for *"God,"* but which should never have been translated that way. The Bible before *"God"* was about something else. Where then does this leave us in terms of understanding El Shaddai? What were the stories of El Shaddai about before they became stories about God? This is the question Cary now puts to me.

"Cary, one way of working that out for yourself is to try a couple of technique to strip away centuries of translation choice. One is to return to the root, etymological meanings and reading them that way, as stories of the Powerful Ones, the Presiding Powerful One, CH-CH, and/or the Destroyer, and just consider if the stories make better sense that way."

Re-reading familiar texts is not easy, and it can take a while to re-frame passages of scripture laden with words we think we already understand. To be fair to Cary I have to reflect that it took me many months of intense study to join the dots, find a new framework and then begin analysing old beliefs and old texts through a fresh lens. I can hardly expect Cary to repeat the exercise within a single conversation. Nor is one tool enough on its own to complete the process. This is the moment when I invoke the midway step boldly taken by the *Edizioni San Paulo* under the guidance of Mauro Biglino, and which Mauro told me about himself over several cappuccinos during my visit to Rome. I wonder if this same approach would assist Cary in his personal studies and if he should ever wish to invite trusted friends or colleagues into a deeper conversation about translation. So, I put it to him.

"Another technique you might find helpful is to leave all these mystifying names untranslated and then simply allow the content of the narratives themselves to show you what they are about. As soon as the God-language is removed, you will find that you begin to evaluate ethically all the action of the stories. Suddenly you are free to call every behaviour for what it really is. And I guarantee you, Cary, that this one tool on its own is quite enough to give you a completely different perspective on what you are reading."

"Try it out and I reckon your respect for our Hebrew forbears will go up several notches. What they originally offered us was a fuller, more layered understanding of the world, and the cosmos. And I think they were very concerned to help us learn from their experience."

However confident I might be of these hermeneutical techniques, I can see from Cary's pained expression that my words have failed to scratch his itch.

"Paul, those tools might work for me personally in my private study, but they don't really give me a way forward in my teaching and preaching, which is where I am really feeling the need for something."

This is a fair comment, and I completely sympathise with Cary's position. People expect their preachers to have a neat and tidy opinion on every mystery and anomaly in the Biblical texts. There is an unspoken pressure on the preacher to have their heads around questions which may have perplexed theologians for generations and to have them resolved by Sunday morning, please! Not only must the mystery be resolved but it must align with all the familiar conclusions and shibboleths of that particular church's sub-culture. So, in no way do I want to trivialize the intellectual chess match Pastor Cary now faces as he considers how to martial all this extra-curricular information about the Bible's ancient narratives.

"Cary, what if for the next little while you shine a light on all the passages in the Bible that offer glimpses into the world of paleocontact, all those texts preachers usually avoid because YHWH is behaving badly, or those awkward passages like John 8 or Matthew 5 and 7, or Luke 11 where Jesus is disparaging YHWH? You know, all those really interesting texts! And what if instead of avoiding them, you read them in church, include them in your bible reading and preaching and then just leave them hanging. Just allow your people time to ruminate on them and join the dots for themselves. Encourage your people to start asking forbidden questions. You can even put model questions into your preaching and then not answer them. Simply leave the questions open."

Cary does not look entirely convinced. It's difficult to divide this process of reframing into bite-size pieces and I can see I have given him more than enough to chew on between now and our next catch up. As our evening concludes he says, *"Paul, I'm going to try that thing where I leave the names in. I know I haven't sat well with reading those names as God for a long time now, but I don't know if I am ready to see dragons and destroyers. So, I am just going to, as you say, leave the names untranslated and just sit with that for a while."*

I am so grateful to have friends like Cary. He is a man of great spirituality, with a truly pastoral heart and great integrity. The fact that he is even willing to speak to me after the publication of *Escaping from Eden, The Scars of Eden* and *Echoes of Eden* is something I appreciate. Many of my pastor-to-pastor relationships have gone rather quiet in the wake of my *Eden* series. It's a mercy that in the parts of the church where I have worked, believers don't generally do shunning. They just stop calling. Although, I have to say, not calling is probably a good deal better than what awaits me in my inbox as I return home to the shipping crate office at the leafy end of my driveway. But that's for the next chapter!

Chapter Eleven

Into the Unknown

Burwood, Sydney, New South Wales – 2015

"Our guest today is one of the best known, most respected evangelical preachers of our time. For thirty years he held the pulpit of one of the world's most renowned preaching centres, held in previous tenures by some the greatest names in the world of evangelical Christianity. We are most fortunate to have him grace our little gathering of pastors here today, half a world away..."

We are indeed very fortunate. My friend Pastor Lance has achieved a great coup in getting Revd. Dr. Darrell Keswick to fly halfway around the world to sit with this small gathering of pastors from across the various denominations in the state capital of Sydney. Lance and I both have great affection for the Reverend Doctor going way back, even if in the years since our spiritual explorations have taken us in rather different directions. I think it would be fair to say that Lance has modelled a lot of his preaching style on that of the reverend doctor.

Early in my career as a priest, I too enjoyed a season of sitting at Darrell's feet, listening to him expound on the scriptures. Darrell was and is a great orator, and I was positively enriched by the experience of watching him in action. However, before long I realized that there was one aspect of his teaching that I felt uncomfortable with. Darrell preached hellfire. And by hellfire Darrell meant eternal, conscious torment. In Darrell's theology the punishment for not becoming a Christian would be that, after your

173

death, God would resurrect you body, spirit and soul, and then set you on fire. Only the agony of being on fire would continue for eternity. This is the classic hell-fire teaching of orthodox Christianity.

I had a problem with this on two counts. Firstly, it is so obviously cruel and unjust. To mete out an infinite punishment for a finite crime is mathematically absurd. The idea that I had a problem with this because I was somehow more compassionate than God was equally absurd. So, something in this overall picture had to be off. My second problem was that it is not the teaching of the Bible. I went to theological college as a relatively new convert from atheism to Christianity. In my first few years as a believer, I had found the churches' arguments for hell as eternal, conscious torment, to be very unsatisfactory and I resolved that a personal goal for my three years of theological training at Nottingham University and St John's College, was to re-read the entire New Testament, scouring it for its teachings about the afterlife to see whether those texts really did teach eternal conscious torment or if there was another way they could be understood. I soon found that the great majority of texts could be read in more than one way and that the plain reading of the majority gave a meaning to do with destruction or ruin.

I quickly saw that Jesus' warnings about ultimate consequences actually have to do with a place called *Gehenna*. Gehenna was the trash heap just beyond the city walls of Jerusalem. Clearly Jesus was speaking figuratively. He was not literally warning people about the municipal trash heap. Rather Jesus was warning his hearers about selfish, destructive, and self-destructive behaviours which have the potential to unravel and ruin your life, and land you on the trash heap of life, full of regret and remorse. When not invoking Jesus' vocabulary around *gehenna*, the authors used

174

other words to indicate the worst possible outcome. They are words which describe being *destroyed, ruined,* or *undone.*

As I continued my fine-tooth journey through the Scriptures, I found only two texts whose plain meaning suggested eternal conscious torment. One is a highly metaphorical text in Revelation full of grotesque symbology, threatening *"those who worship the beast and his image,"* with a perpetually ready funeral pyre. The threat concludes with the phrase, *"And the smoke of their torment goes up forever and ever; and they have no rest day and night..."* The second find was in the Apocrypha, a text in the book of Judith, threatening God's enemies with a perpetually ready fire and a perpetually ready worm to eat their putrefying remains. This is graphic language in an apocryphal book aimed, essentially, at taunting foreigners and infidels. The language is emphatically figurative. To my mind, these two isolated metaphorical texts do not amount to a strong platform for two thousand years' worth of dogma.

Darrell was an enthusiast for the traditional dogma. So, one day in a spirit of humble inquiry, I laid out all the information I just shared with you but footnoted with all the textual references and carefully listing the uses of the key words concerned. I put my findings to him and asked, in the light of these texts, how he had arrived at the conclusions he had championed on an international scale in his books, conferences, and guest appearances. Was the reverend doctor reading the traditional doctrine into the texts or was I mistaken? Were there in reality more than two texts in which the traditional church doctrine could be found without any ambiguity? Was I wrong in my estimation of the openness of the majority of the texts? To give Darrell credit, he answered that he had not really considered the other possible readings of the majority of the relevant texts, those where more than one interpretation can easily be seen. It was something that he hadn't thought to do since he found no conflict between them and the belief he already held. Did it matter that those verses could also support other views?

However, now that I was pressing him, and now that he realised that he couldn't justify his own interpretation over and against other readings of the texts, Darrell told me that he would need to take a little time to re-visit the texts. He would also consult with a more academic friend who happened to be in the process of writing his PhD thesis on the very topic of our conversation. He promised that once he had compared notes with his academic friend, he would be able to get back to me and explain why he had always favoured the traditional doctrine of eternal conscious torment.

At the time I was quietly impressed with Darrell's honesty in admitting that he hadn't even considered alternative interpretations of the vast majority of relevant texts. I respected him for conceding that he needed to put more thought to it before replying and I was more than happy to allow him a little time for the sake of a more developed answer. Twenty-two years later I was thrilled to have the opportunity of a follow up conversation with Darrell while he was visiting Australia. I began by assuring him of my sincere appreciation of his amazing pulpit ministry in my early years. When I asked him how his thinking had progressed on the question of hell since our earlier discussion, this is what he said: *"I have now concluded that you will not find the doctrine of hell as eternal conscious torment in the New Testament <u>unless you already hold that belief a priori before you read all the texts</u>."*

"If you go to the New Testament with a blank slate, you will come away believing that Jesus warned us not of hell but of destruction. But you won't find hell in the Bible unless you already hold that belief. And I hold that belief. Always have! And nothing and no-one will convince me otherwise."

I was open-mouthed. On the one hand I was struck by the reverend doctor's startling honesty while on the other I was simultaneously horrified that he would continue to preach so defiantly on a doctrine that he now admitted he couldn't defend. This lack of a Biblical foundation for such a strong and persistent teaching in the church is the reason why the late, great Revd Dr John Stott, a pillar of British evangelical Christianity, considered hell to be a doctrine that had not been tested against the plumbline of the Gospels and New Testament. Courageously he put this view forward publicly, in his 1988 book *"Evangelical Essentials."* Destruction and Hell are not the same thing. Ruin and regret are not the same as a lake of fire or an eternity of conscious torment. Back in the late 1980's I quietly applauded Dr Stott from the sidelines as he tentatively indicated these rather obvious points.

Unfortunately, despite his unblemished record of decades of orthodox teaching, John Stott quickly found himself pilloried and vilified by fervent evangelical believers all around the world. In fact, he was pressured to such an extent that he finally had to retract his tentative criticisms of the hell dogma, and back away from suggesting that it ought to be tested against the writings of the Gospels and New Testament. Such is the popular zeal for the doctrine among so many Christian believers around the world. It is a zeal which peppers my inbox, unfailingly, every week, and some weeks, every day. As I respond to the comments on my videos and documentaries on *The 5th Kind* and the *Paul Wallis* channel, the graphic threats and hopes of violence to be meted out against me personally by God, provide me with an object lesson in what happens when we confuse the idea of God with a destroyer or a dragon, or some other dark and violent entity. It isn't pretty.

It is only logical. If, in our imagination, we worship a God who exacts violence and genocide, then in our minds we have to justify violence and genocide and call it praiseworthy. If, in our imagination, we worship a God who divides humanity into righteous and unrighteous, then we have to judge people in the same way ourselves. If we worship a God who regards human beings differently according to ethnicity or whether they be *"my people"* or *"not my people,"* we will relate to humanity around us in exactly the same xenophobic way and consider our racism as righteous. Put simply, worshipping a monster makes monsters out of us. The history of invasions, colonizations, executions, witch-hunts, genocides, persecutions, slavery, Jim Crow, and law-enforcement lynchings, all done in the name of *"God,"* is more than enough evidence to confirm the ugly ramifications of worshipping a violent and xenophobic deity.

There is a tragic inevitability to it, that if we confuse brutal colonization with the actions of *"God"* then we will become brutal colonizers ourselves *"in the name of God."* This is why it is critical that we not continue to translate the stories of The Destroyer as if they were stories of God. This is why we should in no way allow ourselves to confuse a dragon story with a God-story. However, merely making the case for that in my books and videos has been sufficient for Christian believers around the world to believe they are thinking in a godly way and doing God a service when they threaten me with the Almighty's eternal, fiery judgement. Of course, they insist, they are not judging me. No, they will leave that to the Destroyer. Good for them!

Of course, I am not the first person in the world to be on the receiving end of this kind of attention. For centuries a horrible eternity has been the stick wagged in the faces of the faithful, to help motivate the people to take the carrot of salvation offered through Christian adherence. Choosing from the two options for your eternal destiny has been the lens through which the Gospel and the New Testament have been read. My friend Pastor Lance would be one of a great number of evangelical preachers who hold a belief in which the Gospel of Jesus Christ is about nothing other than the message of heaven *vs* hell, and if in a single sermon the preacher has not held out the threat of hell with one hand and the promise of heaven in the other then that preacher has simply failed to preach *"the gospel."*

Seen through the polarising lens of heaven *vs* hell, the gospel becomes a message of binaries: *heaven vs hell, worship vs apostasy, obedience vs sin, saved vs unsaved.* Before it became a message of this kind, or at least came to be interpreted that way, I argue that the teachings of Jesus could be seen on a far more invitational and expansive canvas. For instance, the Gospel of Matthew tells us that a phrase Jesus toured with throughout his preaching campaigns was the *"Kingdom of Heaven."* Heard through the traditional matrix of beliefs the term *"kingdom"* conjures up the idea of a feudal dominion in which God is the king and everyone else exists purely to honour and obey him. Once again, by contrast, root meanings offer us a different perspective, in which the Greek *basileia twn ouranwn* could equally be translated as *"The Cosmic Realm."* It would be hard to imagine a more invitational and expansive canvas than that!

Instead, all around the world, in circles Orthodox, Catholic and Protestant, the eternal heaven *vs* eternal hell paradigm has been believed *a priori* (to use Revd. Dr. Keswick's phrase) before needing to read a word of the Gospel and New Testament. For this reason, it might come as a shock to many believers to learn that the very concept of a conscious eternity is essentially absent from the pages of the Bible. The Hebrew word generally translated as eternal is *olam*, and the Greek word *aeon* translates it. However, this is a false translation. Professor Daniel Garrone is one of Italy's most widely respected scholars of Biblical Hebrew and is the co-author of *The Dictionary of Biblical Hebrew and Aramaic*. In its pages Professor Garrone makes the very strong statement that all the great theological dictionaries concede that *olam* does not mean *eternity* and should not be translated that way. Here I have to give credit to my comrade Mauro Biglino who, pointed me to Professor Garrone's contribution, and has encouraged me to add Italian papers, dictionaries and lexicons to my already overwhelmed bookcases. Mauro explains, *"The reason olam has been translated as eternal is because of its association with Yahweh, a word which has been interpreted as God. If he is God, then he must be eternal. If he is eternal, then olam must mean eternal. In other words, it is an invented translation."*

In fact, the words *olam* and *aeon* both carry a meaning that is quite different to the conventional translation. Their actual meaning points us down a completely different avenue to discover a long-forgotten layer of story in the pages of the Bible. Now, at this point, you might think that this is far too much theology for a book about memories of ET contact. You might want to say to me, *"Paul I'm actually not very interested in theology. I'm not a religious person and eternity really isn't something I think about."* And that's fine. But let me ask you this: Are you interested in the cosmos? Are you interested in the nature of the dimension that we occupy? Are you intrigued by the portals represented by the naos carvings uncovered by Roland de Vaux and other archaeologists around the Levant? Earlier I suggested that a naos is what you and

I would call a portal. Would you like to know if the idea of portals or stargates exists in the *The Bible Before God?* If you answered any of those questions with a *"yes,"* then the world *olam* will lead us into some territory that I know you will find fascinating.

If I use the word *dimensions* you might think I'm using language that is exclusive to the twentieth and twenty-first centuries. Perhaps it isn't a concept you would expect to find in ancient narratives or in the Bible? However ancestral narratives all around the world play with the concept of dimensionality, the idea of a plane that is different to ours, somehow occupying the same space and yet somehow beyond the realm of our knowledge and senses. In the Norse myths there exists a dimension occupied by beings more advanced than ourselves, whom we usually don't perceive, and whose plane of existence we are mostly unaware of. Yet what happens in that dimension impacts what happens in this one.

The same notes can be heard in ancient stories of the *Sidhe.* In Celtic thought this was a parallel dimension immediately adjacent to our own, which could impact life in this dimension as we perceive it. Accordingly, the ancient saints and druids of the Celtic peoples developed mystical modalities and shamanic practices intended to tune the practitioner in to the realities of the Sidhe. Aboriginal Australian rituals and narratives of the Dreaming carry identical concepts. So, whether we find ourselves on the southern or northern hemisphere, indigenous traditions can provide us with ancient language for what you and I would call dimensions. In the pages ahead I am going to show you that the word *olam* in the Bible leads us ultimately into the very same territory.

For instance, the Talmud uses the word *olam* and translates it to mean plural *worlds* or *universes*. Think about that! What does pluralizing the word universe imply? The root of the word *olam* points us to the idea of the mysterious unknown. The English language invokes similar concepts of unknowing when we talk about *"The Great Beyond."* It's something we are aware of, yet it's beyond our senses, a realm beyond this world and beyond our knowing. *"The Great Unknown"* indicates something we don't know experientially, yet we know it's there. All those layers are there in the ancient Hebrew usage of the word *olam*. Of course, words can carry different meanings in different contexts, and they can change their meaning through time. So did *olam* ever have an association with time? Or is it a word that only references *the unknown* or *the great beyond?* As it happens, there are passages where *olam* does carry a temporal reference. For example, in the book of the prophet Isaiah from the 8th century BCE we read this:

"I have held my peace <u>me olam</u>. I have been still and restrained myself. But now like a woman in labour I will cry and pant and gasp ..."

The writer says that he has held his peace *me olam - for a time*. He doesn't say how long, but the implication is *"for a long time now,"* or maybe *"for I don't know how long!"* In this instance the mystery lies in when this period of holding his peace began. What is clear, though, is that this period, however long it has been, has now come to an end. *"But now I will cry and pant..."* In that sense *me olam* means almost the opposite of an infinite time stretching into the future. It may be an unknown time stretching into the past, but it is a finite time with a definite end. Indeed, that is the point of the whole passage. His waiting is at an end.

Isaiah 32 uses the word *olam* in a very similar way: *"The palace will be forsaken. The bustling city will be deserted. The forts and towers will become lairs for animals <u>olam</u>...until the ruach from on high comes down."*

Once again we have a reference to a time whose duration is unknown. The city will be deserted for *"nobody knows how long, until..."* The writer is invoking a sense of mystery and the unknown, telling us that the duration of the curse on the city has been concealed, but at the same time reassuring the reader that the curse will end. It will not be forever.

Perhaps I am stating the obvious but by the time I had worked out that the *Gehenna* of Jesus' teaching referred not to Dante's hell but to Jerusalem's municipal trash heap, and once I had learned that the Hebrew word *olam* and its Greek equivalent *aeon* do not point to endless time, I had concluded for myself that the church's threat of eternal hell was a teaching built on a foundation of sand. Today I am fascinated by the direction the word *olam* points us, with its sense of plural worlds or universes, dimensions beyond, unfathomable mystery and journeys into the unknown. This same sense of mystery and concealment is powerfully expressed in a passage in the book of Ecclesiastes. Ecclesiastes 3:11 uses the word *olam* like this:

"The Powerful Ones made everything beautiful in its time. Also, elohim put <u>ho olam</u> in their hearts, so that without exception no one can discover the things that the Powerful Ones have done from beginning to end."

Here *ho olam* is a mystery that nobody can fathom, yet our makers have wired within us a fascination for the unknown, a curiosity which has driven human inquiry and progress from time immemorial. In the C4thCE Plato echoed this belief in his books *Phaedo* and *Timaeus and Critias*, where he makes a case that our ancestors were genetically improved by mysterious other-worldly visitors who fine-tuned us in such a way as to heighten our capacity for intelligence and consciousness. Perhaps Plato and the writer of Ecclesiastes are recalling the same powerful ones and telling the same mysterious story of how it was we first attained our sense of wonder, mystery and curiosity? The same sense of mystery is invoked in Genesis 21:33. *"And he planted in Beersheba at tamarisk tree and there called on the name of Yahweh olam."* Abraham calls on *Yahweh of the beyond,* or *Yahweh the unknown.*

What does this have to do with portals and stargates? I did promise earlier on that these intriguing phenomena would make an appearance in this chapter and you may have been wondering when they are going to show up. In my book *Echoes of Eden* I take some time to probe these cosmic phenomena, theorised by Einstein and Rosen early in the twentieth century, and investigated, measured and flown around by NASA for more than thirty years. These stretching concepts intersect with the Biblical word *olam* in a fascinating way in Psalm 24, a psalm which Monsignor Corrado Balducci believes is all about interstellar travel and paleocontact.

If you are not familiar, Monsignor Corrado Balducci was a senior theological advisor to Pope Benedict XVI at the time of the Pontifical Academy of Science's Colloquium in 2009, regarding the implications of extra-terrestrial contact. Monsignor Balducci's day job is as a senior Vatican advisor in paranormal ministry, entity removal and exorcisms. In 2009 he acquired some extra duties, which involved speaking for the Pope on the question of extraterrestrial contact. In various interviews and statements, Monsignor Balducci insisted that, on the basis of his personal research, people who report close encounters in the present are not describing psychotic breaks. Neither are they entity attachments or demonic experiences. Close encounters are experiences of *"a totally different kind of entity, and one that merits serious study."*

Monsignor Balducci argues that from the very first verse, which implies divine jurisdictions over life on other planets, Psalm 24 is about extraterrestrial contact. Is he right? For me the biggest clue lies not in the first verse of the Psalm but in verse 7 which says this: *"You gates, lift up your heads! And lift up, you doors olam..."* In some auspicious sense, we are opening the doors to the great beyond. They are the doors to the unknown and all is anticipation as we look to see who or what will come from the unknown dimension and arrive through these doors. Having amped up the suspense, the Psalmist finally reveals it: *"And shall come in Melech Hakkavod – the King with his kavod."*

Now what in the world is one of those? Join me in the next chapter as our journey takes us from California to the war-torn country of Syria, where things we learn about *kavods* and the great *olam* will do more than challenge our view of the Bible. It will redefine how we understand our place in the cosmos and the real agenda of our traditional god-figures on project Earth.

Chapter Twelve

The Alien in the Captain's Chair

California – December 2022

Christmas is coming and while I am winding down after an intense season of conferences, summits and live events, my friend Pastor Cary is revving up and preparing himself for a roll of events scheduled for the coming season. Talking hymns and worship songs, Cary is looking for a guest-friendly playlist of music both classic and contemporary. *"I have, Be Glorified, Be Lifted Up, Angels from the Realms of Glory, Gloria in Excelsis Deo, Glory in the Highest..."*

When Cary looks up, he catches my eye and pauses for an instant. *"No, Paul, don't tell me! Don't tell me there's something else going on here?"*

We both laugh. *"Cary, I really don't want to spoil your Christmas, or anyone else's, because after everything I have seen and learned on my research journey, I am still a sincere fan and follower of Jesus. And I love those songs! But since you've asked... What if I were to tell you that the vocabulary of those songs is not language our ancestors created to sing the praise of God? It was the language with which they reported what you and I would call 'Close Encounters of the 5ᵗʰ Kind!'"*

From Cary's bemused reaction, I am pretty sure our lunch is going to be too brief for this conversation to run its course. Perhaps I should have just stopped at *"And I love those songs!?* But since he's asked...I begin with a point that we touched on in an earlier chapter. *"You remember how when our ancestors spoke of the heavens, the heights, the highest, what they were referencing was the sky, or what you and I would call space?"*

Cary nods affirmatively. We are still on common ground.

"Well, tell me, when you picture something being lifted up into the sky, lifted up into the highest heights of the sky, what are you seeing in your mind's eye?"

He ponders for a moment before responding. *"I would imagine a craft, a SpaceX launch, a space-lift, something like that, but that's because I'm a sci-fi guy. I have no idea what the ancients would have imagined."*

"OK then what if I were to ask you if you have ever wondered what 'a glory' is?"

Cary and I have spent a good portion of our churches' worship times singing *"glory,"* especially around Christmastime. However, it's quite possible we have done so without ever really getting to the bottom of what we are actually singing about. What is a glory? In some church circles the word *glory* is used in such a vague way that it means little more than *"Wow!"* To shout *"Glory!"* is to shout *"Wow!"* It is the *"Wow!"* of God. However, in the Hebrew scriptures a glory was something quite specific. It is so specific and objective that in Exodus 33 the writer can tell us that it is here and not there. In Exodus 16 it is in the sky in one moment and on the ground in the next. On Mount Sinai it can be observed moving slowly across the mountainous terrain. It is of a size, apparently, that it can fit through the doors to the unknown in Psalm 24. In the last chapter we left off, waiting for something to come through those doors. We were waiting for the King with his *kavod* – the word we translate as glory. In the coming pages we will see that what comes through those doors is something objective and material. For more detail on this enigmatic *kavod*, we travel to the mountainous region of the Central Negev in the Levant, sometime in the C14th-13thBCE. We are here to witness Moses' famous encounter on Mount Sinai with Yahweh and his *kavod*, as described for us in the book of Exodus, chapter 33. The way this episode is conventionally translated is certainly fascinating. Yet anomalies in the translations clue us that there is something else going on here that we've not quite got to the bottom of. In my previous *Eden* books I have highlighted this passage before. Sitting with the text today I want to revisit this encounter and dig a little deeper into what the words mean and why we should understand Moses as a contactee, and this moment as a close encounter of the fifth kind. The writer tells us:

"Whenever Moses entered the Tent of Meeting, (way outside the camp) the pillar of the cloud would descend and stand near the door of the tent, talking with Moses. And all the people could see the cloudy pillar standing near the door of the Tent of Meeting."

What exactly was it that the people were seeing? Through the ages Bible illustrators have drawn pictures of a pillar made of cloud. But elsewhere this descriptive word *heanan* is translated in ways that would give us a rendering such as *"the pillar of the cloud"* or *"cloudy pillar."* It might be fair therefore to imagine the strange phenomenon not as an amorphous column of smoke but rather as a solid pillar-shaped structure with an accompanying cloud. Exodus 13 points out that by night the mysterious thing would take on the aspect of a *"fiery pillar."* Something else to note is that the pillar does not move along the ground. It is airborne until it lands, vertically, near the Tent of Meeting to communicate with Moses outside the camp. Are you picturing this?

189

Most translations then add words to the verse I have quoted by asserting that the cloudy pillar landed outside the camp by the special tent, and that there *"the Lord"* talked with Moses. However the words *"the Lord"* are nowhere to be seen in the Hebrew text. These words have been inserted into our translations purely because the editors could not imagine how a pillar with a cloud could communicate with Moses. Today I think we could muster answers to that question.

Let's take stock of what has been described. Picture in your mind a pillar which can fly, can also land, vertically, SpaceX style, surrounded by billows of smoke. At the heart of the cloud of smoke is fire, which becomes all the more visible when the pillar is moving at night. Now tell me, what are you seeing? Can anyone say the word, *rocket*? How else would ancient witnesses describe what you and I would call a rocket?

The texts indicate that there were a number of these curious encounters in which Moses would leave the camp, go out to the special tent and communicate with the being, YHWH. After a time, when their conversations have reached a certain conclusion, Moses asks if he can take a look at YHWH's *kavod*. Logically, this question must relate to the only unusual phenomenon in evidence other than YHWH himself. Unmistakably, Moses is asking to be shown the pillar with the fire and smoke, up close.

The conventional translation of Yahweh's reply throws up some problems. *"You can't see my glory face to face because that would kill you"* The problem is that the previous verses have shown Moses in conversation with YHWH for several days, apparently without any difficulties. When Moses asks to see YHWH's kavod, the conventional translation tells us: *"No, because it would kill you, you cannot see my glory. Except when you can. Now that you have asked, you can't. You can't see my glory, but you can see my goodness. However, you can only see my goodness from behind. Although that will be possible only after the mountainside has been cleared of people and animals. Once that has happened, I can let you watch my goodness, from behind, as it moves away from you. However, you will have to be hidden in a cleft in the rock in order not to be killed in the process."*

Let's be frank. That is not a coherent picture. Any reader will be left baffled by that explanation. I say this not out of any disrespect to the translators because I think what has happened to produce this confused picture is that something very specific was described by the original writers, something material and physical, which I would argue was a technological phenomenon. Subsequent generations of Bible translators, who had no technological grid by which to understand what was happening in that moment, then made their attempts to relay the events. However, the translators' paradigm was essentially a religious-spiritual one. In their minds what they needed to depict was a spiritual phenomenon and so they looked for spiritual language with which to describe the encounter. In this way *tub* in the original telling became *goodness*, *kavod* became *glory*, and *paneh* came to mean *face to face*. But as we have already seen, those translations simply don't work. They create an inescapably incoherent picture.

I am going to suggest that the *kavod* moving around Mount Sinai is a craft which, however surprising it may seem, appears to use a rocket-based propulsion system for launching and landing. It is possible that the local flights, such as described by Ezekiel, are referencing the use of a capsule, or module, since its propulsion system appears to be an engine-driven set of rotors, drone-style. With reference to the entire cloudy pillar, the reason that Moses

191

cannot see it *paneh* when it launches is that we are talking about the launch of heavy equipment. Fittingly, the root meaning of *kavod* is a *"heavy thing."*

In the same vein, *tub* is not *goodness* in its root meaning. It is *"the goods,"* that Moses will be seeing moving away from him. Yahweh is talking about heavy equipment. Moses can watch but he will need to be protected in the cleft of the rock. The use of the word *paneh* in the Hebrew scriptures indicates *"in the open, in front of you, in your presence".* These meanings communicate a coherent message. Moses can't be *present, out in the open* when the heavy equipment launches because it would be too dangerous. Yahweh's reply suddenly sounds focussed and eminently sensible. This is what I propose Moses is really being told:

"Moses, you cannot be out in the open when the big heavy thing launches because the blast would kill you. I can let you see the heavy equipment moving as it launches and moves away from you, but you will have to be sheltered in a cleft in the rock."

When rockets are launched from Cape Kennedy, the technicians closest to the launch pad in Florida are three miles away sheltered behind several feet of reinforced concrete The technicians operating the craft itself are in a different state altogether. They're in Texas! So, when Yahweh says, *"You can't be out in the open when the big heavy thing launches or it will kill you,"* it makes perfect sense. It also explains why the kavod's landing place on Mount Sinai, back in the day with Moses, had to be *"way outside the camp."*

The confusion has arisen due to generations of translators who have never seen a rocket launch, who didn't have a technological framework even in mind and were not even looking for one, attempting to describe a technological phenomenon without recognising it. This is why we have a translation which is very unsatisfactory, and which clearly has not got to the bottom of this anomalous technology which exerts a powerful physical impact on the environment, creating so much thrust that the territory has to be cleared of people and animals, and any people nearby will have to be sheltered in clefts in the rock, so the blast won't kill them. You and I are now quite familiar with fiery cloudy pillars which can launch, fly and, post Elon Musk's SpaceX, can then land vertically on a postage stamp. Consequently, we have no problem imagining what's going on here. A twenty-first century eye can look at this picture and say, *"I think I understand what I am being shown."*

If at this point you are still not convinced that the *kavod* is a piece of technology, let's fast forward to the C6thBCE, to territory which today is in the country of Syria where an eyewitness will put nuts and bolts onto what we already know about kavods. Our eyewitness will give us more information regarding its functioning, both during a launch and during flight. The reason this next witness is able to provide so much more detail is that, unlike his ancestor, Moses, he was allowed to do rather more than see it up close. This person was allowed to physically enter the kavod and fly in it. In the next few pages, he will tell us what a kavod feels, sounds and looks like from the inside.

The Kebar River, Syria – C6thBCE

"I looked and saw a stormy wind, which blew from the North, a great cloud with flashing fire and brilliant light around it. In the heart of the fire was a brilliance like amber, and in the middle, what seemed to be four lifeforms. They looked like they had a human form... Now as I watched the lifeforms, I saw a wheel

touching the ground beside each of the four faced life forms. The appearance and structure of the wheels were like glittering chrysolite. All four looked the same and they were structured so that each wheel seemed to have another wheel inside it so that in whichever of the four directions they moved, the wheels did not need to turn... The circumference of the wheels was awe inspiring, and their rims sparkled all the way around. When the lifeforms moved the wheels moved beside them, and when the life forms left the ground, the wheels too left the ground. Because the wheels shared the ruach with the lifeforms." (Ezekiel 1)

This is the first-person report of the prophet Ezekiel. What he describes is a local physical thing. He says where he was when he first saw the kavod. He was by the Kebar river in modern day Syria. He says where the kavod appeared. It appeared in the sky, and Ezekiel describes the sky opening. This language reminds me of the mysterious doors to the unknown beyond in Psalm 24. The skies open and Ezekiel says that the kavod came through a *"searah ruach"* (tr. *whirlwind wind.*) It *"...came out of the north, and from within it a cloud with great raging fire engulfing itself, with brightness all around it radiating out of the midst of the cloud."*

So, we have some really interesting language here, language which is very suggestive to the modern reader. If we peer into the sky, we are peering into space. What does the idea of a hole in space suggest to a twenty-first century imagination? Where does that hole in space lead to? Then by analogy Ezekiel describes something connecting what's on the other side of that hole with the airspace just above the banks of the river Kebar. Would we call this a wormhole? Then from out of the wormhole comes a thing surrounded by a cloud and emitting a flashing light and fire in the heart of the cloud. We have seen one of those before, in Genesis 33 and on the TV!

Next, Ezekiel intrigues us even further by speaking about beings who *"look human."* He says, *"Their appearance was like that of a man."* They looked human. This is a funny thing to say and serves to emphasise that the being in question, while human-like was clearly something other than human. Today, we might say *"humanoid."*

This is probably a good time to mention that the reason that the book of Ezekiel is called *"apocalyptic literature"* is because what the narrator describes is mystifying. The reason is that the writer is himself mystified. So, Ezekiel simply sets out to describe, using whatever references and metaphors he can, what it was that he saw and is still puzzling over. He lays it out as descriptively as he knows how and leaves it to the reader to work out what it was.

Ezekiel goes on to describe the noise that the kavod makes whenever it moves, comparing it to the sound of many waters like a great waterfall. Again, this comparison is not difficult for the twenty-first century reader to imagine. The rumbling, roaring sound of a rocket can easily be likened to the roar of the Niagara Falls, for instance. Just to make the point, when we made a documentary about Ezekiel's kavod a couple of years ago on *5thKind.tv* we played the audio of a rocket launch as the audio track for images of Niagara's Horseshoe Falls and nobody noticed! The sounds are so similar.

Next Ezekiel gives us some detail on the wheels of the kavod and tries to explain how they operate. In my first book on paleocontact, *Escaping from Eden,* I touch on the story of Josef Blumrich, a senior developmental engineer for NASA in the

195

1970s. Prompted by a friendly disagreement with Erich Von Daniken, who had been invited to address a team of senior NASA staff, Blumrich took his engineer's mind to the text of Ezekiel to see what would happen if he produced technical drawings of the wheels of Yahweh's *"glory."* Initially, Blumrich was sceptical of Von Daniken's claim that Ezekiel's encounters were with a technological phenomenon, but as Blumrich drew the schematics for what Ezekiel describes, he was astonished to see a coherent and precise picture taking shape. The result of Blumrich's investigation was the *"Omnidirectional Wheel,"* a design so unique and so practical for craft needing to negotiate unpredictable surfaces, that Blumrich obtained a patent for it, issued on February 5th, 1974, patent number: US3789947A. What Ezekiel saw, now patented, has been equipping NASA's remote rovers from that day to this. So, when I said that Ezekiel's description puts nuts and bolts on our understanding of what a kavod is, it really does! It should leave us in no doubt that the kavod of YHWH, the *"melech hakkavod"* was not what we think of as the *"glory of God."* It was a machine.

Blumrich took his life in hands in 1974 when he published his findings in a book. *"The Spaceships of Ezekiel."* His book went a good deal further than simply identify ancient technology. Not only did Blumrich identify the kavod as technology, he identified it specifically as extra-terrestrial technology and its pilot as an extra-terrestrial being on an assignment relating to Earth's colonization. Given that Josef Blumrich was all the while employed as NASA's Chief Systems Designer in the Program Development Office at the Marshall Space Center, it is interesting to note that his employers allowed him the freedom to publish this kind of literature. Far from censuring Blumrich, NASA promoted and honoured him. Reflecting on his personal turnaround Blumrich later said,

"[When] I began to read Von Daniken [it was] with the condescending attitude of someone who knows beforehand that the conclusions presented can in no way be correct... I have spent the greater part of my life with design and analysis of aircraft and rockets...So I decided to use the statements of Ezekiel to refute Von Daniken and prove the fallacy of his allegations."

Describing how Ezekiel's vocabulary had forced him to reverse his view and find technology in the text, he said, *"Seldom has a total defeat been so rewarding, so fascinating and so delightful!"*

Ezekiel has even more material details for the reader to puzzle over. The writer describes something he calls a throne. A throne is a seat in which the senior person sits when in the place of command. In the context of a craft or a vessel, today we would call it a *captain's chair*. Next, he describes the transparent canopy over the craft, something easier for you and me to understand than Ezekiel, whose experience of glass would have been very limited, and certainly would not have included the forms of flat windows or curved cockpit canopies. In awe, Ezekiel is describing the kavod from the inside. He calls it the kavod of YHWH.

Next, the kavod lifts Ezekiel and the pilot into the air, and as it flies, he notes the physical sensation of vibration and the loud noise the vehicle makes as it moves. As the craft rises into the air, Ezekiel says *"the hand of YHWH was heavy upon me."* How else would a man from the C6thBCE describe the very unfamiliar and disconcerting experience of G forces pushing him down into his seat? Poor Ezekiel had never heard of G forces. It must have felt like an invisible attack, and it was clearly a distressing experience for him, since he tells the reader that he felt bitter and angry while these invisible forces assaulted his body. How could he interpret what for him was a paranormal experience? Something invisible, pressing upon him with that much force, it could only be *"the hand of God."* And he didn't like it!

Next Ezekiel details the places to which he was flown, until finally the pilot puts him down at Tel Abib, where Ezekiel is in such a state of shock that for several days he cannot even speak. How could he not be in shock? This was two and a half thousand years ago, in the period we call the late iron age. Some of the elements of what he saw are technological in nature, the wheels, the canopy, the wings, the vibration, and the sounds. Other elements would appear to be biological entities, such as the captain. There are also other elements which seem to be in some mid-section, where Ezekiel has no idea what he is looking at. A being with human hands, wings, and four human faces, could describe a helmeted, suited humanoid, piloting a personal drone. Or it could be something way beyond any reference point we have in the twenty-first century. Ezekiel simply tries, as transparently as he can, to relay what he experienced, reaching for vocabulary, and reference points from his own iron-age world. His perplexity, which is so palpable in the first-person report he left behind, has invited every reader in every generation since to try and envision what it was that he saw and to find their own explanation.

Consider a reader in the past who had never seen a drone, or an aircraft, a space helmet, or a space shuttle, who had never seen a rocket, and may have never even imagined anti-gravitic technology of any kind. How that kind of reader would understand Ezekiel's descriptions would naturally be quite different to how you and I might understand them. Today however we have a technological framework by which to understand the phenomena in the text, and the amazing story of Dr. Josef Blumrich is a case in point. Today we can listen to Ezekiel, then picture what he is describing and say, *"I think I know what this kavod really was!"*

For further confirmation, Ezekiel 3 reports the prophet witnessing another kavod. *"Standing on the plane, I saw the kavod of YHWH. It was like the kavod I had previously seen by the Kebar river."* This is significant because it clarifies that there is more than one kavod. By this point nobody can think we are talking about the *"glory of God"* in the traditional, vague, religious sense. There is more than one. This second one is also referenced as, *"the kavod of YHWH."* Note, this was the term Ezekiel used to describe both craft. In other words he is using this label to denote the type of craft rather than to specify that the entity YHWH was inside it. In fact, Ezekiel does not identify the pilot as YHWH. Instead, he uses the word *hahyyah* to identify the being who now enters into conversation with him.

Hahyyah is a Hebrew word which indicates a living being. Conventionally it is translated as *creature, living creature,* or *beast.* However, all three of those translations have added an association which is not present in the root meaning. *Creature* implies something that has been created. *Beast* implies something that is animalistic, wild, and strong. However, if all that is indicated by the root is that the being is alive, then I would suggest we have a perfectly good equivalent in modern English in the word *lifeform.* Of course, as soon as a Bible's translation team allows words like *lifeform* into the text or concedes that when the lifeform speaks to Ezekiel it addresses him as *"Human Offspring"* or *"Earthling,"* any attentive reader will be confronted with a heap of pointy questions. A *humanoid* who looks in your face and calls you *"Earthling,"* is clearly not from round these parts. Suddenly we are in the realm of *Star Wars* or *Doctor Who!* The whole tone of the story changes the moment an editorial team admits terms like these (however accurate they may be) into the Bible-reader's lexicon.

Next our *earthling* observer describes the physical shape of the aforementioned *lifeform* in the captain's chair. *"Its shape had an appearance like that of a human-being."* Once again, this is a very curious thing to say. Glaringly, Ezekiel has hesitated to describe the entity as a *human* or a *person*. Today we have terms such as *humanoid*, or *human-like* which might describe Ezekiel's lifeform, except that it is clear that there was something distinctly non-human about the lifeform in the captain's chair. If that were not the case, he would have simply called the captain, a *man*.

Having realized that the kavod parked on the plane in front of him is the same kind of vehicle he had previously been flown in, Ezekiel enters the second craft, which he now identifies using a different word, *ruach*. Some translations express it the other way round and have the ruach entering Ezekiel. However, the order of the words and the sequence of action would imply that Ezekiel sees the kavod, which he then enters in the same way he entered the kavod by the Kebar river, and that once inside the kavod/ruach, he proceeds to enjoy a conversation with the kavod/ruach's mysterious occupant.

Here are some glimpses of his flying experience which follows later in Ezekiel chapter 3: *"Behind me I heard the great vibrating sound of the living things' wings beating against each other, and the sound of the wheels beside them. It lifted me up and took me away... as the hand of Yahweh lay heavy on me. I was taken to Tel Abib, to the exiles where they lived beside the Kebar River. I remained with them in a stupor for seven days."*

200

"Over the heads of the living things was what looked like a solid surface, glittering like crystal, spread out over their heads above them...The noise of their wings when they moved was like the noise of floodwaters, like the voice of The Powerful One the Destroyer, the noise of a thunderstorm or the noise of an army. When they said, 'Stop,' the wings lowered...Beyond the solid surface above our heads there was what looked like a throne made of sapphire high above. Seated on it was a shape with an appearance like that of a human being."

As this close encounter of the fifth kind unfolds, Ezekiel is trying to process the experience in real time. All the while the pilot is attempting to discuss religion and politics with his disoriented passenger. Evidently the captain's agenda was the need to shore up the authority of Yahweh over his designated people group. The lifeform tells Ezekiel that he has been selected to be a spokesperson for YHWH. This is the reason he is being allowed a privileged experience, a V.I.P. trip in YHWH's higher technology. In return for the favour, Ezekiel will be expected to advocate for YHWH and do his best keep the people in line, persuade them not to resist YHWH's governance, and generally be less of a headache for YHWH to manage.

Once again the dark spectre of colonization rears its head in Ezekiel's encounters with these mysterious non-human visitors. The captain, issuing Ezekiel with his orders, reassures his abductee recruit telling him, *"I am not sending you to a people of many difficult ways of speech and whose languages you wouldn't understand..."* In so saying he is possibly implying that this assignment should be easier for Ezekiel than it would be for him. Ezekiel knows these people's languages and ways of speaking. He is the sympatico middle-man between a foreign governor and an indigenous people.

To emphasize the need for a stricter hand of control over the people of YHWH, the captain shows Ezekiel the Temple, flies there, walks him through it, and points out all the reliefs and carvings of the Seba Hassamayim which had somehow survived the great purge under King Josiah. He points out all the other non-human entities still being honoured by the people and priests of that time. But rather than institute another wave of iconoclasm, what the captain now advises is a wave of ethnic cleansing. Any man, woman or child not aggrieved by this commemoration of other non-human beings must be killed, with no pity shown. The captain then issues the order to six officers entrusted with the charge of the people. These officers then disperse to effect the ethnic cleansing, each one using their *keli mashetow* (tr. *destroying thing*.) This enigmatic device is later referred to as the *keli mappasow* (tr. *shattering thing*.) These are the only two instances in the entire Hebrew Canon where this vocabulary is used. Since it only takes six officers equipped with a *destroying thing* or a *shattering thing* to ethnically cleanse a whole district, I don't think it is a stretch to see the *keli mashetow* as a piece of advanced technology, and a nasty one at that. Once again in the long story of colonization we see that it is when YHWH senses his power waning, that the brutality must be ramped up, literally bringing out the big guns, to keep the people in check through executions and terrorisation.

It takes a while for the captain to move his conversation with Ezekiel onto these pressing matters of political control. This is in part because the nature of the encounter, from Ezekiel's perspective, is so far beyond his ability to comprehend. He is so puzzled by the technology surrounding him that he is quite disoriented and distracted, by his own account. While the captain tries to move the conversation forward onto these weightier and more disturbing topics of governance, Ezekiel is all the while distracted by the many strange technological aspects of whatever it is they are flying in and, out of faithfulness to the experience, and maybe to emphasize the otherness of things to do with YHWH, these are the details he carefully itemizes for his later reader:

- the wheels and how they work
- the wings, how they move, and how their functioning responds to voice-commands
- the unfamiliar texture of the wheels, the canopy and the captain's chair
- the noise and vibration every time the kavod moves
- the fact that they are airborne, flying around the country to different sites
- his own state of shock when he was finally put down and allowed to leave

"Cary, if you can accept that a kavod is a craft, which flies from out of space, can land on the surface, and fly a passenger around, doesn't that put Psalm 24 in a different light? 'Let the gates be lifted up!' it says. 'Open the doors to the beyond and let the King's Kavod, enter!' There's a coherent picture here. The kavod is a craft. Olam is the unknown. And as for those doors, I reckon you're either looking at the entrance to a landing pad in a building or what you and I would call a portal."

"Think about it. In Ezekiel and in II Kings when a craft arrives, the first thing that happens is that the 'skies open.' When Jacob encounters the Powerful Ones, coming down from Earth and returning to the sky, they do it via a 'ladder.' Ezekiel's kavod, with its fire and clouds of smoke, arrives via a 'whirlwind wind' and so does Elijah's when it takes him up into the sky, with Elisha

as the eyewitness. Just picture that whirlwind with a craft travelling through it. Don't we call that a wormhole?"

"And it's not the only place in the Bible you can find that kind of concept. In Genesis 11 the writer says the people of prehistoric Babylon constructed something on the Shinar plane, designed to get people to the skies or, perhaps as we would say, into space. The source narrative from out of ancient Sumeria unpacks this aspect of getting people into space. It says that from this construction, fifty technicians had the job of despatching three hundred observers to their stations in the stars. Get the picture? In Genesis it is called 'bab-el.' Those two roots bring together the concepts of gate and power. It could be the 'Power Gate,' or the 'Powerful Ones' Gate.'"

I am pleased to see that Cary is more on board with this idea than I had expected. *"So now you go back to Psalm 24 with the mysterious doors to the unknown, opening up to allow the kavod to enter, and you realise there is a framework for this idea in the Bible which gives us a coherent picture. It shows us that our ancestors had contact with advanced technology in the deep past. They knew what they had seen and heard and sowed descriptions of their encounters into their ancient stories. Since that time, generations of translators have come and gone, translators who had not seen, and not heard. So, they had to take all that rich information, information they didn't recognize or understand, and put it through the filter of their own worldview. Believing they were reading spiritual texts, they reached for spiritual vocabulary. This is one of the reasons why the original layer of first-hand experience became distorted and misunderstood."*

"And don't forget Ezekiel uses the words kavod and ruach interchangeably. He applies them both to the same craft. So

everything we just said about the kavod can be said of the ruach. The 'glory' was clearly technology. Conventionally 'ruach' gets translated as the 'Spirit of God,' but if ruach and kavod can be used interchangeably, where does that leave us in understanding the 'spirit of God?'"

This may seem like a lot of reframing to have to deal with and, like Cary, you might want to sit with it all for a while before settling on any fresh conclusions. We have covered a lot of territory and, though Cary is up for the challenge and very patient with my enthusiasm for the topic, I don't want to overwhelm him with ideas.

"Paul, I think I'm going to do what you suggested before. The elohim, Yahweh, El Shaddai, Elyon, kavod, ruach, paneh, tub, hahayyah, I am going to leave all those words untranslated and then just let the stories speak for themselves."

"That's it!" I tell him. *"Exactly! Just watch and see. How does a kavod behave? What does a ruach do? How does paneh work in the Mount Sinai story? Then ask whether your familiar Bible translation makes sense of the action or if it seems at odds with it."*

We shake on it. *"And then we'll book another coffee!"* We both lean back in our seats as if we have just re-surfaced from an underwater dive. To break the moment, I segue us back to a lighter topic, *"So Cary, back to your list of hymns and songs. What else have you got?"* Cary hesitates before revealing the next song on his list. *"Spirit of the living God, fall afresh on me?"* He looks up for my reaction and takes a sharp breath. *"Are we going to need a beer?"*

I love Cary for his spirit of honest enquiry, the seriousness with which he interrogates his own orthodoxy, and the compassion with which he weighs up how much of his journey he can share with his people. Our NASA friend Josef Blumrich once said, *"Neither he who questions nor he who contributes to finding an answer should be deterred by concern over possible damage to the reputation and professional standing he may have earned by hard work."* I have had to embrace that ethic for myself. On the other hand, every pastor knows the perpetual act of balancing the imperative to stretch a congregation's world with the need to maintain a pastoral relationship. This is the balancing act Cary has to consider as he negotiates the territory we have explored together, and I appreciate his willingness to be sparred with, ever so gently, by a friend on the other side of the event horizon.

On this side of the event horizon, my web of pastoral relationships is largely defined around the area of paleocontact. What that means for me in practice is that my pastoral work today is performed in the main through the open medium of personal coaching. People seek me out through my website and introduce themselves in moments of spiritual emergence, anomalous experiences, or hermeneutical quandaries, but also simply to find a shoulder to lean on through all the regular moments of life transition. So, in a way my pastoral ministry is no different than it has been for decades. Except that today many of those who seek me out have absolutely no interest in and nothing to do with the world of church or institutional Christianity.

When the eighteenth-century evangelist John Wesley was ejected from the Church of England as a result of his anomalous experiences of divine power, Wesley's booming extra-curricular ministry led him to utter the now famous statement, *"The world is my parish."* This is the place I now find myself after my years of travel in the world of paleocontact. In the last few chapters I have shared some of the revelations which have ensured that my coaching now operates well beyond the prescriptive walls of orthodox religion. In the following chapter I will share a discovery which has made it all but impossible for me to read the Bible in the old orthodox way ever again.

As for my next conversation with Cary, the reason a beer might be the order of the day, is that the *"Spirit of God"* of his song-list may prove not be the spiritual phenomenon he imagines it to be once we explore the use of that language in the earliest layers of the Hebrew Canon. In the following chapter we will see that in the *Bible before God* a spirit may manifest as something ethereal in one place, and something very concrete, material, and technological in another. The Bible's word for *"spirit"* is one of those words which has made a long journey in its lifetime – as has its equivalent in many languages. This is what I am about to learn, in the company of a curator of deep ancestral memory, sitting on a sandy beach in the hot and humid extremities of Australia's Northern Territory.

Chapter Thirteen

Joyful Sprits and Close Encounters

Yolngu Country, Northern Territory, Australia - 2023

After two hours of four-wheel driving along loose sand tracks in the hot humidity of what Australians call *"The Top End"* we have arrived at a white sandy beach in Arnhem land. It is a close eighty degrees in this corner of Australia's Northern Territory, but the day is beginning to cool as the afternoon draws on. The turquoise waters of this region provide a rich environment for traditional patterns of fishing, and the fertile areas of bush, which flank the white sand beaches, are plentiful with bush tucker. Here you and I will spend some time in the company of a friend of mine, a young man by the name of Djalu, a member of the Yolngu people. Sitting cross-legged in a shady corner of the hot beach, Djalu will tell us a story that has been told in this place for as long as anyone can remember. It is a story even older than the ancient Sumerian Epic of Gilgamesh. Whereas Gilgamesh is etched into Sumerian clay tablets, this story has travelled through time, from generation to generation, in spoken form. And while the writing of Gilgamesh can be dated to four thousand years ago, this story goes back to the very earliest memories of the Yolngu people, and by today's scientific consensus, the continual cultural presence of Aboriginal Australians on this island continent takes us back at least sixty thousand years into the past.

"In the beginning our ancestors looked around at this great country. They saw the bush full of plants, and the sea full of fish, but they did not yet know how to hunt, or fish, or live in balance

209

with the land. They didn't know what fish were good to eat or how to catch them. They didn't know what bush tucker was for good for food and what was good for medicine. They didn't know what berry could help a woman have a baby, or what other berry would stop her getting pregnant. They could not thrive because they did not yet know the secrets of the land."

When I hear this, my ears prick up. I am expecting to hear of visitors from the Pleiades, people like the primordial tutors of the Cherokee, or visitors like Asherah in *The Bible before God*. However, the language that follows in Djalu's story catches me by surprise.

"When our ancestors were first in this territory there were already beings who lived here. They were very tall, and their bodies were so thin that if they didn't shelter among the trees and the rocks, the wind could blow them away. These were the Mimi. The Mimi were joyful spirits who came and danced with our ancestors. It was from the dance of the Mimi Spirits that our ancestors learned about hunting and fishing. We learned how to recognize the gifts of the bush and how to live a happy life in balance with the land."

What my friend Djalu is telling me fascinates me on so many levels and I truly wish I could stay on this beach for days to soak in the wonder of these ancient memories of *The Dreaming*. By the end of the day, Djalu has given me a great deal to reflect on. The name of Djalu's tribe, *Yolngu* means *from the clay*. This reminds me of the Sumerian narrative of the *Enuma Elish* in which the first modern humans are generated by combining ET DNA with the clay of planet Earth. In the Hebrew version of that story, the root meaning of *Adam*, the prototype human being, is *human*, which means *"of humus,"* or *"made of soil,"* or *"from the earth"* and the

210

story dramatizes that name when the *"breath"* of the powerful one is fused with the *"soil"* of planet Earth. The fact that the Yolngu people describe themselves in the same way catches my attention. Not only does it echo other ancient stories of human origins, it also reflects how strongly the Yolngu people identify with their land. They are part of it. They belong to it.

For that reason I am quite surprised that that Djalu appears to be telling me a story of his people settling into the region, having arrived from somewhere else. But as we talk further, I realise I may have heard wrong. This may not be an arrival story after all. It may instead be the Yolngu memory of the Great Leap Forward. At the heart of the story is the action of the mysterious Mimi as they tutored his ancestors in the cultivation of the local fauna and flora. Surely, that's a *Great Leap Forward* story. Given that the Mimi were already established in Arnhem land, and given that their physical form was so remarkably different to that of the Yolngu ancestors, is it possible that the Mimi were the members of a resident civilization which predated the advent of homo sapiens, and who were ready to assist as soon as the human race became ready?

There is something else besides in Djalu's telling of the story which merits our attention. The Mimi were *"spirits"* yet, at the same time, elements of the story indicate that the Mimi were physical beings. Indeed the peculiar physical build of the Mimi was a big part of what fascinated the Yolngu people and caught their attention. The Mimi's bodies were extraordinarily tall and slender. Furthermore, what they tutored Djalu's ancestors in were physical modalities - hunting, fishing, dietetics, and medication. So what are the Mimi? Are they physical beings or spirit beings?

Djalu's use of the word *spirit* to describe a physical being reminds me that around the world, from culture to culture, the idea of a *spirit* has not always been what it is today. Growing up in post-renaissance, post-reformation Europe, my idea of a *spirit* was of a non-physical being. It could be the non-physical aspect of ourselves. Or it could be a body-less, energy-based being. But globally the concept of a *"spirit"* has a longer and wider lineage than that. As I chew over what Djalu has told me, I reflect that not so far away, in fact just next door in Papua New Guinea, the name *Moon Spirit* refers not to some bodiless energy-being, but to a material being with a particular physical appearance. Exactly what it was is something I will return to in a moment.

The idea of a spirit as a physical being exists in and beyond the cultures of Australia and Papua New Guinea. It is a notion which can be found in the roots of Christian thinking too. One place where this idea makes an appearance in early Christian writing is a theological masterpiece by a famous Algerian Church Father, writing in the early C5thCE. Augustine of Hippo was one of the most important architects of Christian orthodoxy. The subject crops up in his analysis of Judaeo-Christian narratives of *angels.* Augustine's famous work *The City of God,* highlights that the genus, species or biology of angels is something that is never really identified in the Christian and Jewish Scriptures. The word *angel,* he notes, is in fact not a genus or type of being. Rather it denotes a function. To be an *angel* means to be an emissary, an agent, sent to assist, or sent with a message. Those named as *angels* in the ancient texts are material beings. They do physical things, like fight in battles. And they are often noted for an interesting capacity to physically appear and disappear as if by magic. Mirroring the language of the Psalms in the Hebrew Canon, and the letter of Hebrews in the New Testament, Augustine identifies these mysterious physical emissaries as *"spirits"* without regarding that as any contradiction. So we can see that within the Biblical tradition, and the tradition of Christian orthodoxy, there is a track record to the idea of a spirit as a physical being.

As well as in Arnhem land and the Biblical sources, the notion of a physical being which can appear and disappear as if on the wind finds a home in other cultural worldviews. The ancient Greeks spoke of *anemoi* and *aurae* in exactly these terms, and the ancient Romans told parallel stories of the *venti*. Indeed, the very concepts of *spirit* and *wind* are closely connected in many languages and cultures. By association, a being which appears as if from nowhere and disappears to who knows where, might be given the label of *"a spirit"* purely because of that being's mystifying ability to appear and vanish.

Listening to Djalu's story of the Mimi spirits reminds me that what one culture might call *spirits*, another might call *angels*. Another culture might refer to them as the *ancestors*, and still another as *star people*. The fact that they can appear and vanish with such ease puts me in mind of Asherah and her intriguing naos or portal. But why was that association there in the beginning? What was it that first connected the concept of primordial helpers with an idea of beings who could come and go with the wind? To answer that question, we must go back to the moment when our prehistoric helpers first arrived in the account provided in the very first chapter of Genesis.

Southeast Turkey – 9,600 years before present

We are standing on high ground, a craggy island rising precariously above the floodwaters. The dark ocean stretches from here to the horizon. Except there is no horizon. This is because the atmosphere is thick with ash and soot. This pollution is the reason so many are dead, and so little life is left on the remaining pockets of land. We are the survivors and we have only just survived. Life on Earth is nothing like it was before. The whole world has been devastated and laid waste. As it was before, our world was full of life, and full of food, with plentiful sources of clean, fresh water. Now, less than a quarter of the life that was here before remains.

This is planet Earth, some 11,600 years before present on the latter boundary of the Younger Dryas Cold Period, the aftermath of the Clovis Comet impact. When I wrote my first book of paleocontact, *Escaping from Eden*, the research scientists who had pioneered the theory that the Younger Dryas Cold Period was the icy aftermath of cometary impact, were well and truly ahead of the herd. This courageous number included Richard Firestone of the Lawrence Berkely National University, Albert Goodyear of the University of Southern Carolina, and James Kennett of the University of California. It has taken fifteen years for the theory first advanced by Albert Goodyear, with his examination of nano-spherules in North America, to become acceptable in the halls of academia. Yet the memory of this cataclysmic moment in the history of our planet is to be found embedded in world mythology spanning the globe. And, as I argue in *Escaping from Eden*, it is there for the eagle-eyed reader in the first chapter of Genesis.

This picture of the world, flooded, shrouded in darkness and diminished of life can be found in ancestral narratives in Australia, the Philippines, ancient Greece, ancient Sumeria, Peru, Nigeria, Guatemala, southern Benin, ancient Assyria, Akkadia, Babylonia and Sumeria. It was when I discovered for myself the close correlation of details from one indigenous narrative to the next that I first began to consider that this global catalogue of stories might in reality be the curation of ancient cultural memory. If that

214

is so, then the *"creation myths"* recounted by many cultures – the Bible included – are not really creation stories at all. Rather they are the memories of a planetary recovery. What then did our ancestral eyewitnesses see? And what, you may be asking, does any of this have to do with spirits and wind? To answer that question let us return to the primordial scene of Genesis 1.

Above us something enormous is clearing the dark cloud. Powerful winds are driving the darkness away and the light of what we now call *the sun, moon* and *stars* reappear in the sky above the cloud. We have never seen these lights in the sky before. And they are magical. Vortices of wind are emanating from an object in the sky which hovers like a hawk over the floodwaters. These winds then begin to drive seawater away from the higher ground and dry the waterlogged land of the lower-lying terrain. These winds are all recalled in the Nigerian, Beninese, Filipio, Sumerian and Hebrew accounts. They were the product of a technology brought by the helpers when they first arrived to save us in our darkest hour, in that precarious moment when our survival and extinction hung in the balance.

The Hebrew word for the object which hovered and created these winds is *ruach*. Its descendant survives in Ethiopian Amharic as *roha*. The word means a *wind* or *something that creates a wind*. The Popol Vuh, expressing the Mayan account, specifies that the hovering thing which arrived in the dark sky was a craft which carried *The Progenitors* – a word which we could translate as *first ancestors*, but which more precisely means the *originators,* or as one modern translation has it, *The Engineers.* In Genesis 1 the hovering thing is the technology of the *The Powerful Ones.* In this moment of first contact, the earliest ancestral memory recalled in the Bible, the Powerful Ones arrive, as if from nowhere, in a craft that makes wind. From that moment to this, advanced, non-human entities with a highly developed capacity for coming and going, have been associated with wind.

Wind is air. So, it is not hard to see how the word *ruach* might come to be used not only for great movements of air, called *wind*, but also for small movements of air called *breath*. By association, the movement of breath is identified with the life in every living being. A body with no breath is a body with no spirit. By extension we might conceptualize a being with no body, a being which is pure breath, pure spirit. Within the Hebrew Canon, the word *ruach* (just like its Greek counterpart *pneuma* in the New Testament) is used in all these ways. It is a spirit. It is our own spirit. It is our breath. It is the wind. And it is a craft which hovers in the sky, creating winds.

In our traditional translations of the Bible, every one of those meanings is acknowledged but for one exception. The technological aspect of the word, evident in its first appearance, and hinted at by its most fundamental meaning, is excluded. By contrast, a translation approach oriented on root meanings will take us in a completely different direction. If we read the Genesis1 account of the terraforming *ruach* alongside the source narrative from out of ancient Sumeria, we notice immediately that the source narrative identifies *winds* as the primordial terraforming agents operating on a flooded world. It is the *winds* of, the *Enuma Elish*, the Sumerian text, which separate the waters, saltwater from freshwater, and which reclaim the first habitable continent. This comparison with sources allows us a second line of sight on the Bible's *ruach*. This second angle affirms that a material, objective reading is most probably the original perspective.

If we then compare this more physical reading of *ruach* with the action of other world narratives, we find cause to take the view of *ruach* as terraforming technology even more seriously. Moreover, the Bible translator doesn't even have to venture beyond the Hebrew canon to find ruach referenced as a powerful, noisy, wind-making technology. This is because when describing the craft in his close encounter of the fifth kind, Ezekiel uses the two words, *ruach* and *kavod* interchangeably. All the descriptive detail Ezekiel provided with regard to the kavod applies equally to the ruach. Accordingly, a ruach has a transparent canopy and omnidirectional wheels. A ruach can carry a small number of people. It and its capsule can take off vertically and then fly, creating powerful vibrations and making a roaring sound whenever it does. Now, does that sound anything like a spirit, or a breath?

The conventional refusal to allow technological language into our Biblical translations, and the concomitant refusal of our theologians to really engage with the technology of the Bible, is totally at odds with the real scope of the ancient texts. The very action of the texts tells us that the worlds of Ezekiel, Moses, Elijah, Joshua, David, and Saul were worlds populated by human beings alongside non-human visitors, who came bearing powerful and advanced technology. Today we have the vocabulary to express the experiences described by the original narrators. The time is long overdue to allow this vocabulary to cross over from the world of ancient texts and into mainstream conversation. It's about tapping the reservoir of ancient knowledge and bringing what we find into the awareness of everyday people in the twenty-first century. After all, why should translation and editorial boards play gatekeeper with information about our past, information of such vital importance to our understanding of ourselves as a species and our place in the cosmos?

For the time being, humanity's ancestral memories can be found in the folkloric stratum of cultures around the world. It is where

217

we hold our collective memory of traumas in our development as a species, the joy and wonder of benevolent interventions, the wounds of past colonization, and the promise of cosmic assistance. Sometimes the memory of those things is built into our very language. It's to crack open the lid on that linguistic jar that I now travel north of Australia into Oceania. Here, in yet another indigenous source, we will hear the familiar refrain of our ancestors concerning external interventions in our development as a species, and we will find it right under our noses.

Papua New Guinea - December 2022

"More than half a century ago I lived right here, on the banks of the Huon Gulf, in Lae."

We are walking on a beach of yellow sand, with deeply forested craggy mountains behind us and the deep blue of the Pacific before us, quietly lapping the coastline of Papua New Guinea. Our guide, Joan Miller, is an amazing person. She is a graduate of the renowned doctors Professor John Whitman Ray, the pioneer of body electronics, and the great psychiatrist and pioneer of holotropic breathing Professor Stanislav Grof. I could talk to Joan for hours about these amazing fields of research in human health. But today our topic is something else. As we walk the beach together, Joan is generously providing me with a quick-fire education in the language of the local people.

"The beach here in front of my home was a landing point for those who sailed their lakatois (a kind of catamaran) *from further up the coast to the local markets. Depending on the winds, their journeys from the coastal villages to Lae could take many hours. So, I made it my habit to take iced water and cold drinks to the men, women, and children when they arrived. Also, because I had a Land Rover, I was able to provide people with free transport to and from the markets or the hospital as and when they needed."*

218

"As a gesture of thanks, my new friends built a beautiful holiday home for me and my husband in their village of Labu Tale, where we could stay and enjoy the wonderful views of the gulf. It was there, fifty years ago, that my Labu friends taught me what I will now tell you."

The story that Joan now recounts is a tale of ancient memory embedded in the root meanings of everyday words in the Yahapa dialect. This is the language spoken by the Labu people. As she speaks, I begin to wonder how much cultural memory may have been carried in this way by cultures around the world. Joan begins by telling me a story I know - except that I know it from a different source.

Of course my chief source has been the book of Genesis in the Bible. As soon as I re-understood the stories of the YHWH and the Serpent characters in Genesis 3 as the retelling of the Sumerian narratives of Enlil and Enki, I could see that the original meaning of the Eden story in Genesis 3 is the very opposite of what Christian orthodoxy has taught us. Christianity has presented it as *"The Fall"* of humanity from a state of perfection to a state of depravity. Re-reading it today with the perspective of YHWH and the Serpent as representing two elohim / sky people, conflicting over project humanity, reveals Eden to be a place of genetic engineering, in which non-human visitors from the stars, take an innocent being, a primate of some kind, and proceed to clone it in order to upgrade its intelligence and fertility. The upgrade is achieved by splicing human DNA with DNA information from the elohim / sky people.

By the time I met Joan, I had already learned that this story repeats in indigenous narratives all around the world, perhaps most commonly recognized in the ancient Greek, Norse, and Indian narratives. What I did not know was that the Labu people of Papua New Guinea carry a memory of the same intervention in our evolution. More interesting still, is how the Labu people have kept this story alive, and I feel my jaw dropping progressively further as Joan reveals how the same narrative is embedded in the root meanings of the Yahapa dialect's numbers, one to five.

One = *Togwato* = *friends in a ship*

Two = *Salu* = *moon school*

Three = *Sede* = *spirit dance*

Four = *Soha* = *needle and container*

Five = *Maipi* = *spirit goes up*

Joan only has to recite the root meanings for me to see immediately what she is getting at. No further explanation is needed before the penny drops.

Togwato recalls the arrival of our friends from the stars in a ship or canoe. It reminds me of the Cherokee story of friends from the Pleiades who arrive in a craft that looks like an egg.

Salu tells a story just like that of the Mohawk, or the Greek Babylonian story of Oannes, the Book of Enoch's story of the Watchers, the Sumerian story of Shamhat, the Mayan story of Hun Hunahpu, the Hebrew story of Asherah and the Yolngu story of the Mimi. It is the story of our primordial education.

Sede reminds me of the Yolngu description of the Mimi spirits *"dancing"* with his ancestors. It was by their *"dance"* that they spirits interacted with their human companions and passed on their advanced wisdom and knowledge. That's the significance of the *"spirit dance"* to our development as a civilization.

The words *spirit dance* also hint at a more intimate mingling of our ancestors with the visitors. Ancient Celts had the curiously similar word *Sidhe* (pr. *shay*) – which referred to the dimension of

220

the spirits, a dimension intimately close, and which could be interacted with through certain mystical protocols. *Sidhe* and *Sede* are rich words indeed.

Soha – describes an object that is familiar to us in the twenty-first century, but which would have mystified our ancestors. Today a needle plus a container is called a *hypodermic* or *hypodermic needle and syringe*. Our Yahapa-speaking forbears have described for us in simple and direct terms the visual memory of out of place technology witnessed in the deep past. Of course the anomalous presence this ancient hypodermic raises the sharp and pointy question of its function Was this prehistoric injection the moment of modification that upgraded our ancestors? Might it be a totemic reference to a prehistoric laboratory?

Maipi – recalls the departure of our visitors up into the sky, into what today we call *"space?"* Again it echoes the Cherokee story of our ancient visitors' departure in their egg-like craft, ascending into the night sky to return to their home, a planet orbiting a star in the distant constellation Pleiades.

These are not the only correlations that Joan has to show me. For another example, just as the word *ruach* came to mean *Spirit of God* in Hebrew, so in Yahapa the word for God is *Sapakw.* It too is a word with a quite different original meaning.

"The roots of that word," she says, *"...mean Moon Ship."*

Hearing this, my eyebrow elevates several degrees Why would the Labu ancestors even need a word that meant *moon ship*? What on Earth were they seeing that would need to be described that way? And why would they associate whatever it was they were seeing with God? Just as the Hebrew word ruach first appears in the Bible as a piece of technology and gradually morphs into an aspect of God, could it be that before it morphed into a Yahapa

221

word for God a *moon ship* was exactly what it said it was, a piece of technology, an actual moon ship?

Joan now tells me a story which intersects with an indigenous Filipino tradition concerning beautiful non-human others who enchant human beings with the sweet song of their promises and entice them to their underwater bases. Here the human abductees are used for hybridization, enriching their own non-human gene pool with the benefits of human DNA. It is a story I examine in my book *The Scars of Eden*, in which I note that Filipino language is rich with vocabulary whose chief purpose appears to be that of conveying ideas of abduction and hybridization. One of the Filipino words for these beautiful humanoid aquatic entities is *engkantos*. Keep that word in mind as Joan now tells us about a tattoo on a boy's arm.

"One day when I was travelling with some of my Labu friends, I was surprised to see what appeared to be the tattoo of a mermaid. Or at least it was an aquatic-looking woman. The tattoo was on the forearm of a Labu teenage boy. I only knew about mermaids from old English fairy tales, so I was surprised to see that image on the arm of a Labu boy. So I asked him, 'Where did you get this picture from? Did you copy it from an Aussie boy?'"

The boy shook his head. No. This was Labu lore. It was, *"Ekato,"* he said, *"Henasekato."* In the Yahapa dialect *henasekato* translates as *enchanting woman*. The phonetic similarity of *ekato* to *engkantos* reflects a dual connection. The words themselves are related, for sure. So too are the associated stories - anomalous experiences of seduction, which these ancient words serve to describe.

As the afternoon turns to evening we find a street café selling lemon soda. Here they just call it *"Australian Soda"* and it is the drink of choice in this village. It's now dusk, but still warm and humid, and the streets are alive with movement. Cutting across our conversation, Joan suddenly points to a vividly coloured gecko which has just appeared as if from nowhere on the stucco wall beside us.

"Manisapa," she explains. *"Moon spirit."*

As we saw in the last chapter the word *spirit* can be used to describe a physical being which has the capacity to appear as if from nowhere. Given that the gecko has just done exactly that and that, being evening, the moon must be somewhere in evidence, I suggest that perhaps these two factors are sufficient to explain why the gecko might be called a *moon spirit*. However, Joan won't let me settle for that meagre explanation. She hints at another layer of meaning.

"But why 'moon?'" she asks. *"We see the moon in the day, after all!" Why 'spirit?' when it is clearly a flesh and blood animal?"*

These are good questions which prompt me to probe in some other directions. Might the gecko look like something else? Something physical? Something else with a curious capacity to come and go in the blink of an eye? Might the smooth-skinned, almost translucent gecko resemble some other life-form, the memory of which is also buried in Labu language, something that really was a moon spirit? For me, contextualizing the words *"moon spirit"* among other Yahapa vocabulary adds weight to these possibilities. Mentally joining the dots I wonder if the primordial *moon spirit* might have something to do with the *moon school* the *spirit dance* and even, maybe the *needle in a container?* Could it be that the primordial *moon spirit* was a physical being who needed a non-human name, a being with smooth, almost translucent skin, and who travelled with astonishing rapidity between the Earth and the moon in a *moon ship* in a time long ago before *moon ship* became a word for God? Could that be who are what our resident gecko resembles?

Joan Miller's observations are right up my alley. Like Joan, I find vestiges of old knowledge buried in the roots of words which we have become accustomed to translating in other ways. My reframed vision of *The Bible before God* has changed my understanding of our deep past, our present and our future. It has changed the company I keep in my professional life, and it takes me around the world to meet the most interesting people and enjoy the most fascinating experiences. It is why I am, right now, sitting in front of my laptop counting down to the moment I go live in Mexico City.

Chapter Fourteen & Conclusion

The Distant Horizon

Mexico City – January 2023

"I am extremely excited to be introducing to you a researcher, author, and a popular speaker who, across his video platforms, has well over a million subscribers. He puts out some incredible information in connection with world mythology, and ancestral stories which have been shared through history and prehistory. This is what Paul Wallis is bringing to light today."

Whenever a host reads out an introduction like this, I can't help but feel nervous. Have I understood the brief or am I off on a tangent? Will I connect with the audience, or have I misread the room, to be met at the end with an awkward pause and the host announcing, *"And I see we have no questions!"* I always do my best to gauge the scope of the audience and understand the contributions of any fellow-presenters to see where I might fit in, but in conferences as eclectic as this one, this exercise is more an art than a science. My host today, Neil Gaur is a passionate researcher and a popular presenter in the field of the world's esoteric traditions. Today he has gathered an international summit, hosted by his online platform, *Portal to Ascension.* On this platform he brings together incredibly diverse themes and a wide array of researchers and mystical practitioners, and somehow, he always manages to weave their contributions together in a way that sparks people's curiosity and fans the flames of popular exploration, and enquiry.

At *Portal to Ascension* I never know who might be listening in, what are their shibboleths, what their start and finish points might be, what their level of knowledge or faith. Some may be devout religious believers, others sceptics or occultists or humanists. For this reason my presentations are always an act of faith as I attempt to provide a gateway to my topics for literally anybody who might be tuning in with ears to hear.

I quickly sneak in a nervous swig of water before launching into my presentation and seventy-five minutes later I am fielding questions and answers and recognizing a number of familiar faces stepping up to the mic. I see Cary, my mega-pastor friend, lurking anonymously in the online chat window. Tony, my wonderful collaborator on *The 5th Kind TV*, is always in the wings somewhere, checking to see if I'm on form. I can also see my friend in Canada, Omar Faizi, the host of *Watchers Talk*, another eclectic online platform. But the first questioner up to the mic is my conservative evangelical pastor-friend, Lance, always ready for a sparring match and eager as ever to challenge my version of the story of the Bible's formation.

"Paul, when you talk about the evolution of the Bible and the different sources it drew on, aren't you basically parroting the old JEDP theory invented by Julius Wellhausen in the 1800's? Surely by now that whole theory has been completely debunked. Nobody believes that old hat anymore, do they? Didn't the eminent Professor, Eta Linnemann do a statistical analysis on the language of the Old Testament more than thirty years ago, which totally discredited Wellhausen's and your version of the Bible's history?"

This may sound like a hopelessly involved and academic question, and I can't help feeling that Lance has, in a spirit of friendship, carefully crafted his question to bog me down in paragraphs of apologetics. Biting my lip, I am doing my best to resist the urge to give Lance a book's worth of commentary to defend my theological *bona fides*. But this is not a theological summit, and I

226

am anxious not to put my audience to sleep. So I do my best to muster a reasonably brief summary of an answer.

"Thanks Lance. What's called 'JEDP theory' is all about identifying the Bible's sources: J stands for Yahwist, E for Elohist, D for Deuteronomist, P for Priestly. Now, it would fair to say that the theologian you mentioned, Julius Wellhausen didn't invent the idea of sources. The French Professor Jean Astruc was writing about the sources of the Pentateuch a full hundred years before in the seventeen hundreds. Wellhausen simply set out to explore what had been understood in principle for generations."

"Also, it's not at all controversial to say that the Bible came together in stages, that there was a time before the Nevi'im (the greater and lesser prophets) for instance, when there was only the Torah. Now, it's only logical that if the Hebrew tradition begins with Abraham and Sarah, we should expect to find its roots in the culture from which Abraham and Sarah originated, that being ancient Mesopotamia. For that reason, in the early stories of the Torah we would fully expect to find the evidence of Mesopotamian sources. Every priest and pastor who studies theology has to learn about sources and consider where the texts came from and what they were before. That's part of our basic theological training."

"For an example of redaction, it's easy to see that a post-Moses writer has re-told the stories of the Pentateuch. That's why the name YHWH which was first revealed to Moses appears in stories which long pre-date Moses. The original stories have been re-told by a narrator who knows that later name. The narrator doesn't hide what he's doing. It's all done in plain sight. So I don't think that's in any way controversial. Even a casual reader can see that the books of the Deuteronomistic history include the re-telling of stories, because all the action has an editorial commentary layered over the top of it. And the editorial comment imposes moral judgements which clearly post-date the action."

I did intend to be brief, but I am on a roll.

"For an example of that, think about the Noah story. For Noah there was no such thing as 'clean and unclean animals' because the clean and unclean laws come from a time aeons after Noah, from the time of Moses. So, when the narrator says that the Ark was populated with animals 'clean and unclean,' you know straight away that you're reading a writer from after the time of Moses commenting on a much older story. Again, the redactor is giving himself away."

"Then for another layer to the flood story, just take note of the numbers of those animals entering the ark and you will be able to work out that Genesis 6 has actually sewn together two tellings of the flood story, one from a writer who believed in clean and unclean animals, and one from a writer who didn't. So in the flood narrative you've got at least two sources and one redactor weaving the sources together. Earlier sources and later redaction, OK?"

I can't hear Lance saying anything. So, I take that as permission to continue.

"You mention Eta Linnemannn. What she did was critique the nineteenth century source critics like Wellhausen for their analysis of vocabulary and word-frequency. That's fair enough. Nineteenth century scholars didn't have the kind of software tools that we have today. So maybe they missed a trick or two in their modelling. Fair comment. But to be fair to Wellhausen, the basic idea that the Bible as a whole was formed as a compendium of earlier sources which were then edited together, that core part of the JEDP story is absolutely solid."

This is as much detail as I want to lay on the audience eavesdropping my conversation with Lance, but for your benefit let me just add that, having boldly defended Julius Wellhausen just now, I do differ from him on a couple of points. Because the Bible's elohim (*powerful ones*) equate with the anunnaki (*sky people*) of the Sumerian source narratives, my logic is that the elohim narratives most probably constitute the original source layer. I would then argue that while the name YHWH may belong in very early narratives, YHWHism as an editorial layer (which source critics call J) first appears at the formation of the Pentateuch, which as a separate canon of books may not even have existed before the final redaction of the texts in the C6thBCE.

This then compresses the timeframe for a Deuteronomistic edit and a Priestly edit. It is possible that D and P may represent sources, or even redacted sources. But they aren't necessarily redactions of the whole canon. So, it is possible that before the C6thBCE, the Hebrew canon existed not as a defined list but as a library of diverse sacred texts, and that the work of bringing them all together and harmonizing them as best as possible, was done in one almighty process.

Having reasoned my way to this conclusion about the formation of the Bible, I find I am not the first to see it this way. In the nineteenth century, German theologians Karl Heinrich Graf and Wilhelm Vatke drew precisely the same conclusions through their own analysis of how the layers and fragments of Hebrew story were sewn together to create the Bible as we know it. At theological college I remember reading these three scholars rather dismissively. In my youthful headspace, I considered their contributions as no more than an almighty distraction to the real work of preaching the Gospel. Only decades later, after my own travels in hermeneutics and translation, have I returned to voices I previously dismissed, recognizing that they and I have landed independently on very similar territory. In a way it gives me a sense of reassurance not to be the first person to have published the views I have shared with you in the previous thirteen chapters. Cary now throws in a question about the Jewish mystical tradition of Kabbalah and Bible code.

"Paul if there is esoteric information layered into the Bible as we have it, and codes carrying prophetic information, doesn't that negate what you are saying about editors having cut and pasted it all? Surely an untidy process like you describe would mess all the patterns up."

This is a great question. My research has not gone into the mysteries of the Kabbalah, nor into the claims of Michael Drosnin's famous book, *The Bible Code.*

"Hey Carey! No, what I am saying doesn't negate those things at all, although those are not my areas to be honest. What I am saying would simply mean that much of the esoteric information encoded into the texts as we have them, would have been the work of the theologians who produced the final redaction."

My friend Omar now asks me about the dreaded *C word*, a word I hesitated to put in the title of the book you are now holding.

"So, Paul, are you saying the whole Bible as we have it is in reality one giant conspiracy?"

Conspiracy can be a really unhelpful word. On the one hand the story in I Kings 22 about the prophet Micaiah remote viewing the Sky Council, reminds us that information can be hidden, that people can be deceived, and that even nations can be tricked into proxy wars. This is a significant kind of warning worthy of careful reflection.

At one time it was a conspiracy theory that the Gleiwitz bombing was an inside job to trick the general public and justify totalitarian rule in pre-war Germany. At one time it was a conspiracy theory that the tobacco industry was paying doctors to lie about the health risks of smoking. It used to be a conspiracy theory that the corn and sugar industries paid for disinformation about healthy fats in order to sell more corn and sugar-based product. It used to be a conspiracy that J Edgar Hoover was a cross-dresser, or that Liberace was gay. I could go on.

The fact that we have official secrets laws tells us straight that there are such things as official secrets. The very existence of these laws signals that there are layers of information, the revelation of which would challenge official narratives and explanations. Why else would we have such laws? Certainly, in times of international conflict, any efforts to foreshorten wars, involving classified communication across enemy lines, will require the public to know one thing and military intelligence another. For example, when I was a boy, it was a conspiracy theory to suggest that behind closed doors the British government was secretly in conversation with the leaders of the provisional IRA. *"We don't talk to terrorists,"* was the constant mantra of Downing Street. Later this mantra was proven to be false, and because of the progress since, many of us are thankful for that. Nevertheless, the previous solemn assertions of *"official sources,"* including more than one British prime minister, were ultimately revealed as nothing more than cover stories.

What is covert politics? It means things like domestic governments doing business behind closed doors with enemy powers or selling armaments to non-allied nations, or major donors sponsoring both sides in an election in return for guaranteed kickbacks, or news media promoting corporate-sponsored *"news,"* or banks profiting from both sides of a war. For the general public, the ninety-nine percent, awareness of this kind of politics is unsettling. But unaccountable parties and

231

processes shaping our geopolitics are a fact of life and awareness of this realpolitik has by now made its way well and truly into the light of day.

"Omar, I think the truth is that every government communicates with its people on a 'need-to-know basis,' and in a need-to-know world, until classified files are declassified, official secrets revealed, or embargoed news released, all such information will always be shaded by official sources as 'speculation' or 'conspiracy theory.' That's just the way of things.

For all those reasons, I think the language of *conspiracy theory* is profoundly unhelpful. Most importantly, it undermines the most courageous of our journalists, whose very job is to interrogate official narratives and hold authorities to account. The language of *conspiracy* deters and disempowers that kind of inquiry, and, in the end, it represents a deeply anti-democratic ethic.

"I believe that as human beings we should be constantly curious. Surely curiosity is our greatest asset as a species. It has been the spark of every scientific and technological advance in history, and the precursor to every bit of social progress. Who or what are we as homo sapiens if we cannot wonder and ask questions? In a democracy we expect it of our academics, scientists, and journalists. In a free society, people should always have the liberty to challenge official narratives and petition for information."

As I pause for breath, I pick up on a pause on the Canadian microphone. It's my friend Omar, patient as always.

"I couldn't agree more, Paul, but my question was, "Is the Bible as we have it today really just a great big conspiracy?"

I swallow hard. *"O.K."* I am on the spot and there is no escape.

"Short answer: 'Yes!'"

I take a deep breath because I know I am about to offend a lot of people and I really don't want to. I just have to do my best to honour the texts of the Bible and the scribes who have brought them to us, while also exposing a neglected side to their story. Measuring my words as carefully as I can, I continue.

"Yes, the Bible is a conspiracy in the sense that the final redactors deliberately set out to cover up the full spectrum of Hebrew ancestral memory."

"These are vital and detailed memories concerning humanity's great leaps forward and the role played by extraterrestrial interventions. The redactors did their level best to airbrush that whole layer out of the picture. In that sense, yes, we have to say there was a cover up of vital information. A key part of their commission was to blackout the textual evidence of our upgrade from hominids, references to previous civilizations, or ET entities and technology encountered by our ancestors, and of information concerning a continuing program of hybridization. So a cover-up? Yes, absolutely."

"Having said all that, I don't think it is fair of us to demonize these redactors. The ancient scribes probably believed what they were doing was good and godly. Their logic was that they were cleaning up what they understood to be superstitions and pollutants from their enemy cultures. The Ten Commandments from Moses taught the people not to depict other powerful ones, and Moses' successor Joshua told the people to cut themselves off from other powerful ones. I imagine the redactors felt they were following those commands to their logical conclusion by applying them to the sacred texts themselves. If they were convinced YHWH-ists, then to their own thinking there was an integrity to what they were doing."

"In the end though, this re-write meant covering up who and what we were in the beginning. It meant denying our primate roots and demonizing ET contact and intervention. "

"The Christian church then continued this process of reframing. It cast Eden as a place of innocence first and then of rebellion against God - for which everyone of us is now guilty and worthy of hellfire. This of course is what puts us in need of the ministrations of the Church. It's a message that's very useful for managing believers and empowering religious leaders, but it's all based on a falsehood. Eden is not what we have been told. And we human beings, post-Eden, are so much more than we have ever been allowed to know."

Within Christianity, the suppression of paleocontact was taken even further when the Imperial Church glued the Hebrew canon onto a selection of apostolic writings to create a Christian Bible of Old and New Testaments. Christian orthodoxy was then militarized in 318CE, when Emperor Theodosius effectively made himself head of the Imperial Department of Religion, by intervening to settle a theological impasse, and passing a law to illegalize *"pagan"* (ie non-orthodox) religion. The emperor's new position as Defender of the Faith put him over the Christian bishops as a spiritual authority. The bishops were now positioned within the fabric of the empire as the spiritual counterparts of the senators, with the plebeian faithful beneath them, meekly praying and obeying. Rather like King Josiah's manageable theocracy, this was now a manageable theocratic empire with Christianity as its religious gloss.

In the centuries since, every invasion and colonization by Rome's imperial heirs and successors would mean extinguishing non-Christian cultures like the Brazilian, Guatemalan, Peruvian, Nigerian, Kenyan, Ghanaian and Celtic, each of which carried their own lore concerning paleocontact, ancient technology, genetic engineering, and draconian non-human governance in the deep past. So, yes, there has been a long-lasting conspiracy of suppression.

Still more recently, within Christianity at least, there has been a conspiracy of silence surrounding the ancient Mesopotamian stories of paleocontact on which so many of the Biblical narratives are based. The Bible's dependence on the Sumerian, Babylonian, Akkadian, and Assyrian accounts of Anunnaki has been known in academic circles since 1872, when English Assyriologist George Smith discovered the world's oldest story, etched in cuneiform script on one of the then two hundred thousand clay tablets awaiting translation in museums around the planet. His work of translation opened a window onto a world of forgotten times and cultures, and shone fresh light on the meaning of the elohim narratives of the Bible. Suddenly the plural form of the word *elohim* in the Biblical texts made sense, and we had a little more detail on who and what these Powerful Ones of ancestral memory really were.

In the 1890s Professor Nathanael Schmidt of Colgate and Cornell Universities further demonstrated the significance of the relationship of the Biblical stories to memories of Mesopotamia. Sadly, in the one and a half centuries since these discoveries were promoted within the academic world, this vital information about the nature of the Bible's elohim has remained confined within the bounds of university and seminary faculties, only rarely allowed out into synagogue and church communities, and scarcely if ever making an appearance in the teaching and preaching of communities of faith. In this way senior clergy, prelates, popes, theological educators, and seminary faculties have been privileged with one set of information, while people of faith faithfully attending synagogues and churches are offered something else entirely. This is a great shame.

I am far from the first person to talk about this divorce of information. Back in the 1990's I lived in London's Camden Town. During my tenure, a priest by the name of Dave Tomlinson, became the vicar of the adjacent parish, St Luke's Holloway. Dave is known for writing a book called *The Post-Evangelical*. In it he argued that many, if not most evangelical believers would be first horrified and then positively enlightened if their pastors would open up about the knowledge they had gained by studying the Bible at degree level. In short, he was calling out this eerie divorce of information which allows discoveries made in the nineteenth century, which totally reframe our understanding of the Bible, to remain almost completely unknown to the vast majority of Bible-readers.

However, to be fair to my comrades in the world of ministry, it would not be accurate to characterize this divorce as a deliberate conspiracy. The dynamics of church life are such that the congregation or local eldership often see it as their role to teach the pastors and keep them on track rather than the other way round. The congregation or eldership board become sentinels watching for any error that might creep into a pastor's sermon from time to time. (Every week I receive letters and online comments from people who see their role this way.) Stray from the script and most priests and pastors will be either roundly ignored or swiftly corrected – no matter what respect or credibility they may have accrued through their lives of study and teaching. Remember what happened to John Stott when he questioned the shibboleth of hell. Consider my friend Cary as he calculates how much information he can reveal before anything he says becomes irrelevant to his large and faithful flock.

Before getting anywhere near the hairy implications of Judaism and Christianity's God-stories being based on memories of ET contact, many pastors find they are not free even to share fundamental information about the Bible's possible sources and gradual formation. This is for fear of bursting the bubble of a fundamentalist view which regards the Bible as if it were dictated verbatim by *"The Almighty"* and which considers applying any kind of intellectual approach to the Bible as a kind of sacriledge. Just as a devout person must remove their shoes before walking onto sacred ground, so any kind of intellectual enquiry must be surrendered before handling the holy book.

Furthermore, because many churches gather on the basis of a canon of shared beliefs and doctrines, the power of groupthink can be very strong. It is a dynamic which diminishes people's sense of permission to ask their deepest questions or bring their best insights. One must always defer to *"what the group thinks."* This leaves the curious person stifled and silenced by the over-riding ethic of not rocking the boat. By this logic a group can only be as courageous as its most fragile member. This is why you will always have to scratch well beneath the surface before you will discover a congregation's true diversity of belief, speculation, and experience. It is why when I visit churches I find that people will often sidle up to me and tell me with a wink and a whisper that they watch the *Paul Wallis* channel or *The 5th Kind TV* or that they have read one or other of my books. They do this as if they had just confessed to some kind of naughty secret. Whatever a group's intention, the power of taboo over the best part of two millennia ensures that a congregation's real depth and breadth is seldom expressed in the public life of our communities of faith.

Neil is still fielding calls. *"On the line now is Tetteh, who joins us from Ghana. He has a question about what motivates you to write your books about ancient ET contact."*

"Hi Tetteh, nice to meet to you!"

"Good Morning, Reverend! First of all, congratulations on all your books and on gaining more than a million subscribers. That is very good. I can see you are very, very busy, putting your content about! On the other hand..."

...Here it comes...

"In your previous life in your ministry in the churches, for thirty-three years you influenced thousands of people in the direction of mainstream Christian orthodoxy. Now you are working like a busy bee, pushing people away from mainstream Christian beliefs. You are extremely busy. The Eden Conspiracy is your fourth book about ancient aliens. I think you have a hundred and fifty or more documentaries on your channels. Are you busy, leading people astray? Or are you working so hard these days because you want to make amends. Are you doing penance for the three decades you spent misleading people?"

Ouch! I can see Neil Gaur, shifting in his seat and wanting to leap to my defense, but I jump in first because our caller has asked a fair question. It's something I have put some thought to and I am more than happy to give an answer to.

"Wow Tetteh! You have asked a very probing question. I would say that as a teacher and a writer, I have always sought to do three things:

- *Spark people's curiosity and appetite to look closely at the ancient sources for themselves*
- *Provide people with tools and resources to help them plumb the texts with their own questions*
- *Share my own learning journey*

To that end I have always made a point of highlighting the problems and anomalies for my hearers to wonder at, even and especially when I didn't have an answer!"

"Yes, certainly, what I believed when I started out as a young preacher and writer is different in many ways to what I believe today. Thankfully 'what I believe' has only ever been one aspect of my teaching. Those first two elements have always been far forward in the mix for me - and I can assure you that people have always felt free to disagree with the 'what I believe' part of the equation. Same today! You should see my inbox every morning! So, Tetteh, you may be overestimating my past influence!"

"As to making atonement or doing my dharma for having misled people in the past, I guess you could see it that way. The way I see it is that it would be irresponsible of me, having spoken so much in the past in support of one perspective, not to speak in the present about my more recently developed perspective. As a habitual teacher, though, it is more a matter of I 'can't not' continue to share the journey."

"My sense of urgency in putting out books and documentaries arguing for a paleocontact reading of the Bible is not calculated in proportion to my own role in supporting a YHWHist or fundamentalist view in the past. I do it because the implications for our psychology as a species and our ability to tap potential as human beings are so great, and the momentum of the traditional YHWHist or fundamentalist understanding of God, Jesus, and the Bible, is so huge."

"In my coaching I have met so many people whose lives have been hurt by the taboo around these topics, that I deeply desire to break that taboo, simply by arguing for paleocontact and a populated

239

universe in a calm and hopefully persuasive way. And it is such a powerful relief and release of energy when people experience the kind of reframing I argue for in my Eden series. That kind of energy from people all around the world spurs me on."

"I think now is a time for other voices to be heard and for narratives and sources we may have dismissed in the past to be given a more respectful hearing. For all those reasons I don't want to waste my time and I don't want us to waste our time in this fascinating life."

Neil Gaur's audience today on *Portal to Ascension* is certainly a diverse one. It's a diversity which reflects the wide range of people who contact me every day through my website. My correspondents include pastors and denominational leaders who have seen the same things I have seen in our ancient texts and have drawn the same conclusions. They want to know how to move forward in ministry while at the same time carrying all this extra-curricular information. I hear from contactees and experiencers of close encounters of the first to fifth kind who are trying to process their experiences, discern the real from the unreal, and come to a new understanding of the world in the light of their experiences. I hear from veterans of war, Iraq in particular, who speak about the ancient technology of another civilization, and who are thinking through what the implications of that might be. They are just one group of friends with privileged information who like to nudge me and encourage me to keep going. And I will keep going in my research path, despite all the threats of eternal hellfire to be inflicted by *The Destroyer*, whom some of my religious correspondents like to call *"God."* I appreciate my brothers and sisters' zeal and concern, some of them, but after decades of hermeneutical study and travel through the world of root meanings, that is no longer how I conceive of

240

God. Omar now puts a question to me which has visited me with increasing frequency over the last couple of years.

"Paul, these are dark and worrying times for many when we look at the agenda of the powers around the world. You talk about the hidden hand of corporate power. It certainly seems to be pushing things in some disturbing directions right now. From where I am sitting, powers behind the thrones seem to be oriented toward goals that perhaps may not be so great for the great majority of us. How does your 'before God' reading of the Bible speak to that? Does your vision of paleocontact offer people any hope?"

This is a vital question and I agree that these are disturbing times. Certainly, it isn't hard to notice a subtraction of freedoms of choice, information, and expression from the grassroots, while progressively more wealth and power is centralized to the one percent, gathered in the halls of big media, big tech, big pharma and the big banks. These trends have only intensified over the last couple of years of international emergency. It's a visible trend which can leave regular people feeling overwhelmed and totally overpowered. But the *Bible before God* speaks to a spectrum of powers at play in project humanity, and I have found that a journey into root meanings opens that spectrum up to examination via the lens of our ancestors.

The Bible Before God bears witness to a diversity of Powerful Ones, reflecting a spectrum of agendas, civilizations, and regions of space. When we interrogate *The Bible Before God* with regard to this non-human layer of governance, the news is not all darkness and doom. Yes, on the one had there are certain menacing and draconian powers like El Shaddai, the Destroyer. However, on the other hand there are also more benevolent powers like Asherah, the Lion Lady and her cohort, who elevate and empower humanity, equipping human beings for a fuller and more enjoyable experience of life on Earth. The stories of this

241

cohort, memorialized in the names of Asherah, Hun Hunahpu, Oannes, Shamhat, Mbab Mwane Waresa, remind us that among the powers of the cosmos are beings ready to protect, equip and uplift humanity. So, when we read Jesus' words in Matthew's gospel announcing that *"The Powers of the Cosmos are at Hand"* it is worth remembering that these beautiful, generous, pro-human entities are among those cosmic powers. I don't think we would be anywhere present on Haim Eshed's galactic council if we didn't have allies in high places.

This was part of the worldview of the Greek precursors to Christianity, and many of the Church Fathers, and writers of the first Christian literature. They considered help to be available and not just to those in high places but to each and every person. For instance, when the writer of 1 John 4 refers to the contact experiences of early Christians, it is contact with helpful entities that he wishes to promote. To follow the writer's lead and engage with such help, we must first be willing to surrender any idea that we are the lone intelligence in an empty cosmos. We have to acknowledge that we are in company if we are to follow his teaching and weigh up what the *"spirits"* have to tell us. Similarly, we need a public acknowledgement that we are already in contact if we are to engage as a civilization with Haim Eshed's *"Galactic Council"* and do as Dr Ed Mitchell called for by *"[taking] our place in the community of space-faring civilizations."* I applaud the work of courageous people like the late Dr. Mitchell who shine a light on the reality of contact phenomena today.

It is why I wholeheartedly commend Professor Brigadier General Haim Eshed for bringing his information into the open. Ignorance is powerlessness and knowledge is power. Back in the day, King Josiah and his followers didn't want their people knowing that cosmic contact and help were potentially available to ordinary human beings. To their thinking subjection to YHWH - El Shaddai was all that was needed to keep society compliant and manageable in the C7thBCE. Could it be that the powers today have made a similar calculation? In all this, my reason for hope is that our ancestors still speak.

Read with the hermeneutic I have argued for in these pages, and throughout my *Eden* series, our ancestors speak clearly about cosmic helpers and their availability to humanity as a whole, and to you and me individually. If you are interested in exploring what that kind of contact might look like, get hold of a copy of *Echoes of Eden* in which I sit at the feet of the traditional guardians of indigenous cultures for the wisdom of the world's oldest ancestral narratives.

A couple of years ago, in a conversation on *The 5th Kind TV* with Erich Von Daniken, the granddaddy of contemporary paleocontact theory, he told me that from his background in Jesuit education, he believes that if we were to translate more fundamentally no more than ten key words in the Bible, the extraterrestrial layer of its story would be inescapable. I hope the journey you and I have shared in these pages has demonstrated that to be true. We have taken time with the root meanings of *elohim, elyon, el shaddai, YHWH, seba hassamayim, olam, kavod, ruach, hahyyah, basilea, ouranwn,* and *Asherah*. This etymological approach to cutting through layers of translation and cultural association has revealed an earlier canon of information. Through that lens that we have seen a wider, less religious, and more civic education in what our Hebrew forbears left to us. They wanted us to be socially intelligent, wise to the persistence of old powers and aware of patterns of covert government and hidden hands in political life. They wanted us to discern the non-human layer in geopolitical affairs and understand the dangers of false information, or of artificial fears cynically stoked to manipulate nations into fighting pointless proxy wars, or to manipulate populations into factionalism and xenophobia. Our ancestors wanted us to be emotionally smarter, not disempowered and fragmented by fear, not stirred up and herded by demagogues. In the dramas of their story and in the object lesson of the Great Coup and the Great Redaction, they left us warnings about the dangers of centralized power and the editing out of every narrative other than the official one. Their narratives reveal dangers on the one hand and reasons for hope on the other. In their view help is at hand, just as it was for our ancestors in the time of Asherah. All in all our ancestors wanted us to have a better human experience than they did. This is why they recorded what they did, and it is why they didn't pull their punch by skirting around the vital topic of paleocontact. To their mind, this was information for the public domain.

For that reason, I am enormously grateful to many who carry this kind of privileged information today. I mean people like the late Ed Mitchell and Paul Tellyer, Dimitri Medvedev, Chris Mellon, and Haim Eshed. I applaud courageous high-profile people like these who have challenged the longstanding policy of secrecy and censure. Each one I have named has spoken up in the hope that we, their hearers, will pay attention, join the dots, and allow a fuller to picture to form. Friends like these encourage me to keep going.

I am grateful for your company too. I realize that I may have stretched you to the point of discomfort, or if you have read other titles in my *Eden Series*, I may have prevailed on your patience by revisiting certain themes you and I may have visited before. However I think that by this page you will probably have formed a shrewd idea as to why I have chosen to bring these particular chapters together. My hope is to make the case to an increasingly wide demographic that the Bible is not what most people think it is. Before it became a book about God, the Bible was a book about human origins, paleocontact, contact in the present, and the truth about human potential – both at an individual level and at the level of a more conscious and intelligent society. I hope that you have enjoyed the ride and that, having read this book, you might leave your copy on a friend's coffee table, or better yet, buy them their own copy! Taboos are broken only when people like you and me are willing to risk an embarrassed laugh or a raised eyebrow by broaching stretching subjects.

En Route

Today, we are headed out into deeper territory and denser jungles. We will venture further out towards the edges of our oceans marked on antique maps with the famous legend, *"There be dragons."* What kinds of dragons might we encounter as we travel further? Could they be real flesh and blood beasts, veiled in dark smoke and brimming with fiery menace? Will they be the mythical dragons of Egypt, Mesoamerica, Georgia, and Japan, Draca the *"wyrm"* in the Saxon Beowulf, or the deadly foe of the Armenian Saint George? Or might they be more sympatico, like the dragons of Disney or Avatar? Perhaps we will face other kinds of foes besides, the behemoths of injustice and oppression, doled out by compassionless elites. Who knows?

To journey into the unknown requires a certain willingness to question our ready-made conclusions. Sometimes we may need to revisit places and people we may previously have dismissed or disrespected. Reflecting on my own journey to this point, I can vouch that the pathway of unlearning and reorientation requires a good measure of discomfort and patience. It is not for the faint-hearted.

At six in the morning, the roads are still quiet. Yet even at this early hour, it is already a steaming, hot day. Crammed full of sweating bodies, young and old, the interior of our rattling bus is even steamier. The passenger next to me is a middle-aged woman who has clearly come well-equipped. I note what looks like an army-grade backpack and a canvas bag full of bottles of water. The children to the other side of me look peaceful and resigned to the hours of swaying and bouncing that will fill our time between now and our arrival at the next stop.

I stare through the bus and out through the window to the accelerating blur of buildings, people, vegetation, and dusty pot-holed roads, abutted by sheer cliff faces and precarious drops, and I note that the valley below is dotted every now and then with the carcasses of long-deceased vehicles which somehow must have underestimated the sharpness of the turn. I breathe in deeply, accepting the prospect of the voyage ahead. Since it is good not to journey alone, I hope that you will join me as the road ascends, winding us ever higher into wilder, rockier country. Whatever the discomfort *en route*, I know it will be worth our while for the sake of reaching new locations and making new discoveries. Perhaps we will return with stories and artefacts which will provide a new window onto our distant past and guide us further as we look ahead to the future. I hope you will come with me. But be prepared. It's going to be a long journey.

Made in the USA
Las Vegas, NV
13 October 2023

78735369R00143